Somatic Therapy Workbook

Exercises to Treat Trauma, Complex PTSD and Dissociation

Mindfulness, Self-Compassion, and the Mind-Body Approach to Reduce Stress and Heal Trauma

Yevhenii Lozovyi

ISBN Print: 978-1-962027-27-4

ISBN Kindle: 978-1-962027-28-1

A Note from The Author

I hope this book will benefit you in your journey to increase your happiness and quality of life!

If you have not claimed your bonus exercise manuals, do not hesitate to email with a request. They will help you on your journey!

Note: *How to request additional exercise manuals*

Email *the subject line:* **The Book Title + exercises request.**

I do not spam! I only strive to provide value. For example, I only email monthly with a free Kindle book offer when Amazon allows me to schedule a promotion. Many books are in work now, and if you find the subject interesting, you will have a chance to receive the Kindle version for free. My main interests are mental and physical health, biohacking, and everything else that can increase happiness and quality of life.

Constructive criticism is always welcome! I am always looking for ways to improve the quality and accessibility of the materials. Feel free to reach out to

yevhenii@fiolapublishing.com

If you find this book helpful and could benefit others, please leave a review on Amazon. It would mean a word to me if you do so.

Best wishes,

Yevhenii

Table of Contents

INTRODUCTION

APPLICATIONS OF SOMATIC THERAPY

Somatic therapy is a powerful and transformative approach to healing that recognizes the profound interconnectedness of mind, body, and spirit. By working directly with the embodied experience of stress, trauma, and emotion, somatic therapy offers a pathway to deep and lasting change. It helps individuals release patterns of tension, restriction, and disconnection and cultivate greater resilience, vitality, and wholeness.

In this chapter, we will explore some of the key applications of somatic therapy, focusing on four common areas of struggle: PTSD and C-PTSD, anxiety and depression, grief, and chronic pain. Through a combination of theoretical understanding and practical techniques, we will see how somatic therapy can help alleviate suffering, promote healing, and support individuals in reclaiming a sense of agency, empowerment, and embodied well-being.

PTSD AND C-PTSD

Post-Traumatic Stress Disorder (PTSD) and Complex PTSD (C-PTSD) are debilitating conditions that can arise in the aftermath of severe or prolonged trauma. Characterized by symptoms such as hypervigilance, intrusive memories, emotional dysregulation, and a pervasive sense of fear or shame, PTSD and C-PTSD can have a profound impact on an individual's quality of life and sense of self.

Somatic therapy offers a unique and effective approach to treating PTSD and C-PTSD by directly addressing the ways in which traumatic experiences become encoded in the body. Through techniques such as titration, pendulation, and the completion of survival responses, somatic therapy helps individuals process traumatic memories gradually and safely, allowing for the discharge of bound traumatic energies and the restoration of a sense of safety and equilibrium in the body.

Titration involves working with small, manageable doses of traumatic activation rather than overwhelming the nervous system with intense or prolonged exposure. By carefully calibrating the level of arousal and ensuring adequate time for integration and stabilization, titration helps to prevent re-traumatization and supports the gradual building of resilience and tolerance.

Pendulation refers to the natural oscillation between states of contraction and expansion or between activation and settling. By learning to track and allow this organic rhythm, individuals can develop a greater capacity to ride the waves of intense sensation and emotion without becoming overwhelmed or disconnected.

Completing survival responses involves facilitating the release and resolution of thwarted or incomplete defensive actions, such as the impulse to fight, flee, or freeze in the face of threat. By providing opportunities for these responses to be expressed and discharged in a safe and supported way, somatic therapy helps to uncouple the association between the traumatic event and the body's protective reactions, promoting a greater sense of agency and empowerment.

In addition to these processing techniques, somatic therapy also places a strong emphasis on building somatic resources and regulating neurophysiology. This may involve practices such as grounding, centering, and self-soothing, which help to promote a felt sense of safety and stability in the body. By strengthening the capacity for self-regulation and resilience, somatic therapy supports individuals in navigating the challenges of PTSD and C-PTSD with greater ease and adaptability.

ANXIETY AND DEPRESSION

Anxiety and depression are two of the most common mental health challenges faced by individuals today, and they often go hand in hand. While the specific causes and manifestations of anxiety and depression can vary widely from person to person, they are often characterized by patterns of chronic tension, constriction, and negative self-belief.

From a somatic perspective, anxiety and depression can be understood as states of persistent body armoring or bracing, in which the musculature becomes habitually tight and contracted, leading to feelings of heaviness, fatigue, and emotional depletion. These patterns of tension may serve as a form of self-protection or defense against perceived threats or stressors. Still, over time, they can become self-perpetuating and limit an individual's capacity for joy, connection, and vitality.

Somatic therapy offers a range of techniques and practices for working with anxiety and depression, with a focus on releasing chronic muscular tensions, regulating arousal levels, and restoring embodied experiences of safety, ease, and openness.

One key approach involves the use of mindful movement and self-massage to identify and release areas of holding or bracing in the body. By bringing gentle, curious attention to these patterns of tension and experimenting with small, incremental shifts or adjustments, individuals can begin to experience a greater sense of spaciousness, flexibility, and flow in their physical and emotional experience.

Another important aspect of somatic work for anxiety and depression is the cultivation of interoceptive awareness, or the ability to sense and track internal bodily sensations. By learning to attune to the subtle cues and signals of the body, such as changes in breath, heart rate, or muscle tone, individuals can develop a greater capacity for self-regulation and emotional balance.

This may involve practices such as body scans, which involve systematically bringing attention to different regions of the body and noticing any sensations or feelings that arise without judgment or analysis. It may also involve more active forms of engagement, such as exploring the qualities of movement that feel most nourishing or expansive or experimenting with different postures or gestures that promote feelings of openness, connection, and vitality.

GRIEF

Grief is a natural and inevitable part of the human experience, arising in response to loss, change, or transition. Whether it is the death of a loved one, the end of a relationship, or a significant life upheaval, grief can be a complex and overwhelming experience with profound impacts on both the mind and the body.

From a somatic perspective, grief is often experienced as a felt sense of heaviness, constriction, or emptiness in the body, as if the magnitude of the loss weighs down the very cells and tissues. There may be feelings of tightness or pressure in the chest or throat, a sense of disconnection or numbness, or a pervasive sense of fatigue and depletion.

Somatic therapy recognizes that these physical sensations are not simply byproducts of the grieving process but are an integral part of how we experience and process loss. By bringing compassionate attention to the bodily experience of grief and allowing space for the full range of sensations and emotions to be felt and expressed, somatic therapy can support individuals in moving through the grieving process with greater ease and resilience.

One key approach to working with grief somatically is using movement and expressive arts. By engaging the body in gentle, fluid movements, such as swaying, rocking, or stretching, individuals can begin to release some of the physical tension and stagnation that often accompany grief. Similarly, by exploring creative forms of expression, such as drawing, painting, or sculpting, individuals can give form and shape to their inner experience, helping to process and integrate the complex emotions of loss.

CHRONIC PAIN

Chronic pain is a complex and debilitating condition that affects millions of people worldwide and can have profound impacts on physical, emotional, and social well-being. Unlike acute pain, which serves as a protective signal of injury or illness, chronic pain persists long after the initial cause has resolved and can become a source of ongoing suffering and distress.

From a somatic perspective, chronic pain is understood as a multidimensional experience involving a complex interplay of physical, emotional, cognitive, and social factors. Rather than simply being a localized sensation in the body, chronic pain is seen as a systemic response to perceived threat or danger, involving patterns of tension, bracing, and hypersensitivity that can become self-perpetuating over time.

Somatic therapy offers a range of approaches for working with chronic pain, with a focus on reducing physical and emotional suffering, releasing bound survival energy, and promoting more adaptive ways of relating to and managing pain.

One key aspect of somatic work for chronic pain is the practice of mindfulness, or the ability to bring present-moment awareness to the bodily experience of pain without judgment or reactivity. By learning to observe and accept the sensations of pain, rather than resisting or fighting against them, individuals can begin to develop a more spacious and flexible relationship to their experience and to find moments of ease and relief even amid discomfort.

This may involve practices such as body scans, which involve systematically bringing attention to different regions of the body and noticing any sensations that arise, or breath awareness, which can help to regulate the nervous system and promote a sense of calm and relaxation. It may also involve more active forms of engagement, such as gentle movement or stretching, which can help to release tension and promote circulation in areas of chronic holding or bracing.

Another important aspect of somatic work for chronic pain is shifting cognitive-somatic pain maps or the patterns of neural wiring that underlie the experience of pain. By providing new and different forms of sensory input, such as touch, movement, or visualization, somatic therapy can help to interrupt and reorganize these patterns, promoting greater flexibility and adaptability in the nervous system.

KEY SOMATIC THERAPY TECHNIQUES

At the heart of somatic therapy lies a profound understanding of the brain's remarkable capacity for change and adaptation, a process known as neuroplasticity. This concept has revolutionized our approach to healing trauma and cultivating emotional resilience, offering a pathway to rewire the patterns of the past and embody a greater sense of safety, vitality, and wholeness in the present.

Somatic therapy recognizes that our experiences, whether nurturing or traumatic, shape the very structure and function of our nervous system. When we undergo a distressing event, our body's natural survival responses can become stuck or overactive, leading to a range of physical, emotional, and behavioral symptoms that can feel overwhelming and difficult to manage.

However, targeted somatic techniques and practices can interrupt these cycles of reactivity and build new neural pathways that support greater regulation, resilience, and choice. By engaging with the felt sense of our embodied experience, we can gently release the residual impact of trauma and reconnect with our innate capacity for healing and growth.

One of the foundational principles of somatic therapy is the cultivation of body awareness, or the ability to tune into the subtle sensations, impulses, and cues of our physical being. This embodied self-awareness is essential for developing a strong and coherent sense of self, as well as the capacity to navigate our relationships and life choices with clarity and agency.

Through practices like grounding, which involves sensing our contact with the supportive surfaces beneath and around us, we can enhance our proprioception or our ability to feel our presence and movement in space. This can be incredibly stabilizing for a dysregulated nervous system, helping to anchor us in the here and now and mitigate sensations of overwhelm or disconnection.

Another key somatic concept is pendulation, which refers to the natural oscillation between states of contraction and expansion, activation, and settling. A resilient nervous system can fluidly move between these poles, much like the ebb and flow of the tides or the flutter of a bird's wings. By gently encouraging this organic pulsation, we can build greater flexibility and adaptability in our stress response.

Titration is another central tenet of somatic therapy, which emphasizes the importance of working with small, manageable doses of activation rather than flooding the system with intense or overwhelming sensations. By carefully regulating the pace and intensity of our trauma processing, we can avoid becoming mired in what is known as the "trauma vortex" and instead cultivate the resources and resilience of the "healing vortex."

As we begin to release the bound energy of trauma through somatic techniques, we may experience a process of sequencing or the organic unfolding of physical sensations and emotions. This might manifest as a wave of tension rippling through the body, a spontaneous tremor or shake, or an upwelling of grief or laughter. By allowing these authentic expressions to move through us, we can integrate and transform the previously stuck or fragmented aspects of our being.

Underpinning all of these somatic practices is the art of resourcing or intentionally connecting with experiences of safety, support, and nourishment. When we have undergone trauma, our threat detection systems can become overactive, constantly scanning for signs of danger, even in benign situations. By consciously cultivating sensations of groundedness, stability, and connection, whether through affirmations, relational attunement, or evocative imagery, we remind our nervous system that it is possible to experience challenges and still recover a sense of equilibrium and ease. Part I: Foundations of Somatic Therapy

Additional Techniques Utilized in this Workbook

HEART RATE VARIABILITY BIOFEEDBACK (HRVB): A POWERFUL SOMATIC TOOL

In the ever-evolving landscape of somatic therapy, it is essential to incorporate tools and techniques that resonate with a wide range of individuals. While practices like mindfulness, body scans, and embodied movement have proven invaluable for many, some may find it challenging to gauge their progress or stay motivated without a more tangible, measurable approach. This is where Heart Rate Variability Biofeedback (HRVB) comes in as a powerful addition to the somatic therapy toolkit.

WHAT IS HEART RATE VARIABILITY BIOFEEDBACK?

HRVB is a cutting-edge technique that involves monitoring and training the body's natural heart rate variability (HRV) – the fluctuation in the time intervals between consecutive heartbeats. By using specialized biofeedback devices, individuals can learn to consciously regulate their HRV, which is closely linked to the autonomic nervous system and overall well-being.

When we experience stress, anxiety, or trauma, our autonomic nervous system can become dysregulated, leading to a host of physical and emotional symptoms. HRVB helps to restore balance by teaching individuals to activate their parasympathetic nervous system, which is responsible for the "rest and digest" response. Through guided breathing exercises and real-time feedback, HRVB enables users to optimize their HRV and cultivate a greater sense of calm, resilience, and self-regulation.

THE BENEFITS OF HRVB

Research has shown that regular practice of HRVB can lead to a wide range of benefits, including:

1. Reduced stress and anxiety: By training the body to respond more adaptively to stress, HRVB can help alleviate symptoms of anxiety, panic, and chronic stress.

2. Improved emotional regulation: HRVB has been shown to enhance emotional self-regulation, enabling individuals to better manage intense feelings and impulses.

3. Increased resilience: By strengthening the body's natural stress response system, HRVB can help build resilience in the face of adversity and challenge.

4. Enhanced cognitive function: Studies have found that HRVB can improve attention, memory, and overall cognitive performance.

5. Better sleep quality: By promoting relaxation and reducing hyperarousal, HRVB can help improve sleep quality and alleviate symptoms of insomnia.

6. Reduced symptoms of PTSD: HRVB has shown promise as a complementary treatment for post-traumatic stress disorder, helping to regulate the nervous system and process traumatic memories.

A CLEAR AND STRUCTURED APPROACH

One of the key advantages of HRVB is its clear and structured approach. Unlike some other somatic practices, which can feel abstract or difficult to measure, HRVB provides a concrete, data-driven framework for tracking progress and reinforcing positive change.

Through the use of biofeedback devices, individuals can see their HRV in real-time, with clear visual displays and audio cues guiding them towards optimal breathing patterns and physiological states. This immediate feedback loop can be incredibly motivating, as users can directly observe the impact of their practice on their nervous system and overall well-being.

Moreover, HRVB allows for quantifiable progress tracking over time. By regularly monitoring HRV metrics such as coherence, amplitude, and frequency, individuals can objectively assess their improvement and identify areas for further growth. This can be particularly appealing for those who thrive on structure, accountability, and measurable results.

INCORPORATING HRVB INTO SOMATIC THERAPY

While HRVB is a powerful tool in its own right, it is most effective when integrated into a comprehensive somatic therapy approach. By combining HRVB with other embodied practices like mindfulness, movement, and self-inquiry, individuals can cultivate a deeper, more holistic sense of mind-body connection and self-regulation.

For example, one might begin a session with a brief HRVB exercise to regulate the nervous system and establish a sense of grounding and presence. From there, they could move into a mindful body scan, using the heightened awareness and coherence cultivated through HRVB to more deeply attune to subtle sensations and feelings. Finally, they might engage in a somatic movement practice, allowing the body's innate wisdom to guide them towards greater integration and embodiment.

By weaving HRVB into the fabric of somatic therapy, we can offer individuals a powerful, personalized toolkit for navigating the ups and downs of life with greater ease, resilience, and self-mastery. Whether used as a standalone practice or as part of a more comprehensive approach, HRVB has the potential to profoundly transform the way we relate to ourselves, our bodies, and the world around us.

A NOTE ON HEART RATE VARIABILITY BIOFEEDBACK (HRVB) AND ACCESSIBILITY

While the practice of HRVB has traditionally relied on specialized clinical equipment, it's important to note that this powerful technique can also be made accessible to a wider range of individuals through the use of more readily available devices.

In recent years, the proliferation of wearable technology has made it easier than ever to monitor and track heart rate variability (HRV) in real-time. Devices such as the Apple Watch, Fitbit, and other sports activity trackers that measure pulse can provide a convenient and affordable way to engage in HRVB practice, without the need for expensive or hard-to-obtain clinical equipment.

These consumer-grade devices typically use photoplethysmography (PPG) sensors to measure changes in blood volume and calculate HRV based on the intervals between heartbeats. While they may not offer the same level of precision as professional-grade ECG monitors, they can still provide valuable feedback and support for individuals looking to regulate their nervous system and cultivate greater resilience and well-being.

Moreover, many of these devices come with companion apps that offer guided breathing exercises, real-time HRV monitoring, and other features designed to support HRVB practice. By syncing the device with the app, individuals can access a wealth of data and insights into their physiological state and track their progress over time.

It's worth noting that while these consumer-grade devices can be a valuable tool for HRVB practice, they should not be seen as a substitute for professional medical advice or treatment. Suppose you have a pre-existing health condition or are experiencing significant symptoms of stress, anxiety, or trauma. In that case, it's important to consult with a qualified healthcare provider before starting any new self-care practice.

That being said, the increasing accessibility of HRV monitoring technology is an exciting development for the field of somatic therapy and one that holds great promise for empowering individuals to take a more active role in their healing and growth. By leveraging the power of these readily available devices, we can help make the benefits of HRVB practice more widely available and support more people in cultivating greater self-awareness, self-regulation, and resilience in the face of life's challenges.

This paper provides a systematic review of the use of Heart Rate Variability Biofeedback (HRVB) as a treatment for conditions like depression, post-traumatic stress disorder (PTSD), and anxiety disorders.

Neurophysiological Approach by Self-Control of Your Stress-Related Autonomic Nervous System with Depression, Stress and Anxiety Patients.

BY: Kees Blase, Eric Vermetten, Paul Lehrer, and Richard Gevirtz

https://www.ncbi.nlm.nih.gov/pmc/articles/PMC8036915/

https://www.mdpi.com/1660-4601/18/7/3329

THE SCALE OF BODY CONNECTION (SBC): A FRAMEWORK FOR DEEPENING EMBODIMENT

In addition to the powerful tools of HRVB, this workbook also introduces the Scale of Body Connection (SBC) as a structured approach to guide your journey of embodiment. The SBC provides a framework for understanding and cultivating progressively deeper levels of mind-body integration, moving beyond superficial body awareness into the realms of profound somatic transformation.

THE SBC CAN BE UNDERSTOOD AS A CONTINUUM OF EMBODIED EXPERIENCE WITH FOUR DISTINCT LEVELS:

1. Body Awareness: This foundational level involves the basic noticing and tracking of physical sensations, functions, and experiences in the body. Most people operate at this level of awareness much of the time, attuned to the surface-level signals and cues of their physical being.

2. Embodied Presence: At this level, individuals begin to fully inhabit the lived experience of their physicality, cultivating a deep, sustained presence within the body. This involves a shift from merely observing the body to actively engaging with and abiding within the felt sense of embodiment.

3. Psycho-Somatic Processing: Here, the mind-body connection becomes a focal point of exploration and integration. Individuals actively work with the interplay between their thoughts, emotions, and somatic experiences, using the body as a gateway to access and process deeper psychological and emotional material.

4. Embodied Transformation: At the deepest level of the SBC, individuals tap into the transformative potential of fully integrated embodiment. This involves catalyzing profound, multi-dimensional shifts in one's way of being, perceiving, and relating to self, others, and the world. The body becomes a vehicle for spiritual growth, healing, and awakening.

Throughout this workbook, you will be guided on a journey along the SBC continuum, with each section building upon the skills and capacities of the previous levels. The practices and explorations in the early chapters will help to establish a strong foundation of body awareness and embodied presence. At the same time, the later sections will invite you to venture into the depths of psycho-somatic processing and embodied transformation.

As you progress along the SBC path, you may find yourself "descending" into new territories of your being, accessing hidden resources, wisdom, and potential that lie within the somatic realm. This journey of embodiment is not always easy, as it requires a willingness to face and work with the full spectrum of your human experience, including challenging sensations, emotions, and memories that may arise.

SCALE OF BODY CONNECTION: A MULTI-SAMPLE CONSTRUCT VALIDATION STUDY

CYNTHIA J. PRICEE LAINE ADAMS THOMPSON, SUNNY CHIEH CHENG

PUBLISHED: OCTOBER 13, 2017

HTTPS://DOI.ORG/10.1371/JOURNAL.PONE.0184757

HTTPS://WWW.NCBI.NLM.NIH.GOV/PMC/ARTICLES/PMC5640211/

HTTPS://JOURNALS.PLOS.ORG/PLOSONE/ARTICLE?ID=10.1371/JOURNAL.PONE.0184757

PROGRESSIVE MUSCLE RELAXATION (PMR): A FOUNDATIONAL SOMATIC PRACTICE

Progressive Muscle Relaxation (PMR) is a classic stress-reduction technique that has earned its place as a foundational practice in the world of somatic therapy. Developed by American physician Edmund Jacobson in the 1920s, PMR is based on the simple yet profound principle that physical relaxation can lead to mental and emotional calm.

The practice involves systematically tensing and relaxing different muscle groups throughout the body, typically starting with the feet and moving upwards toward the head. By intentionally creating and releasing tension, individuals learn to recognize and let go of the physical holdings that often accompany stress, anxiety, and trauma.

THE BENEFITS OF PMR

Research has consistently shown that regular practice of PMR can offer a wide range of benefits for both physical and mental health. Some of the key advantages include:

1. Reduced muscle tension and pain: By actively releasing tight, contracted muscles, PMR can help alleviate chronic pain conditions and promote overall physical comfort.

2. Lowered stress and anxiety: PMR has been shown to reduce symptoms of anxiety and promote a greater sense of calm and relaxation.

3. Improved sleep quality: By promoting physical and mental relaxation, PMR can be an effective tool for combating insomnia and enhancing sleep quality.

4. Increased body awareness: Through the process of systematically engaging with each muscle group, PMR can help individuals cultivate a deeper, more nuanced sense of body awareness and interoception.

5. Enhanced emotional regulation: By learning to release physical tension, individuals can also develop greater capacity for letting go of emotional and mental holdings, promoting overall well-being and resilience.

WHY INCLUDE PMR IN A SOMATIC THERAPY WORKBOOK?

Given its wide-ranging benefits and accessibility, PMR is a natural fit for any somatic therapy workbook. As a gentle, non-invasive practice that can be easily learned and applied, PMR offers a valuable entry point for those new to somatic work, as well as a reliable resource for more experienced practitioners.

Moreover, PMR can serve as a powerful complement to other somatic practices, such as breathwork, mindfulness, and embodied movement. By providing a structured, systematic approach to physical relaxation, PMR can help individuals establish a sense of safety and grounding in their bodies, which can then support deeper exploration and processing of emotional and psychological material.

Including PMR in a somatic therapy workbook also honors the fact that different individuals may resonate with different practices and approaches. For some, the concrete, step-by-step nature of PMR may feel more accessible and effective than more abstract or open-ended techniques. By offering a diverse range of tools and practices, we can create a more inclusive and personalized path towards embodied healing and growth.

DIAPHRAGMATIC BREATHING: THE FOUNDATION OF EMBODIED REGULATION

Diaphragmatic breathing, also known as belly breathing or abdominal breathing, is a simple yet profoundly effective technique that lies at the heart of many somatic therapy practices. By learning to breathe deeply and fully into the belly, individuals can access a powerful tool for self-regulation, stress reduction, and emotional balance.

The diaphragm is a large, dome-shaped muscle located at the base of the lungs. When we breathe deeply into the belly, the diaphragm contracts and flattens, allowing the lungs to expand fully and take in a greater volume of air. This type of breathing is often associated with a state of relaxation, calm, and groundedness – in contrast to the shallow, chest-centered breathing that often accompanies stress, anxiety, and fear.

THE BENEFITS OF DIAPHRAGMATIC BREATHING

Research has shown that regular practice of diaphragmatic breathing can offer a wide range of benefits for physical, mental, and emotional well-being. Some of the key advantages include:

1. Reduced stress and anxiety: Deep belly breathing activates the parasympathetic nervous system,

which is responsible for the body's "rest and digest" response. By shifting the body into a state of relaxation, diaphragmatic breathing can help alleviate symptoms of stress, anxiety, and panic.

2. Improved oxygenation and circulation: By allowing for a fuller, more efficient exchange of oxygen and carbon dioxide, diaphragmatic breathing can improve overall oxygenation and circulation in the body.

3. Enhanced emotional regulation: Deep breathing has been shown to have a calming effect on the amygdala, the part of the brain associated with emotional reactivity. By regularly practicing diaphragmatic breathing, individuals can develop greater capacity for emotional balance and resilience.

4. Increased body awareness: The act of breathing deeply into the belly can help individuals cultivate a greater sense of connection and attunement to their physical sensations and needs.

5. Improved digestion and elimination: The gentle massaging action of the diaphragm on the abdominal organs can help stimulate digestion, relieve constipation, and promote overall digestive health.

WHY INCLUDE DIAPHRAGMATIC BREATHING IN A SOMATIC THERAPY WORKBOOK?

Given its wide-ranging benefits and accessibility, diaphragmatic breathing is an essential inclusion in any somatic therapy workbook. As a foundational practice that can be easily learned and integrated into daily life, belly breathing offers a powerful tool for self-care, stress management, and emotional regulation.

Moreover, diaphragmatic breathing is a versatile practice that can be used in conjunction with many other somatic techniques, such as progressive muscle relaxation, mindfulness meditation, and embodied movement. By establishing a deep, calming breath as a anchor and resource, individuals can more easily navigate the challenges and intensities that may arise in the course of somatic exploration.

Including diaphragmatic breathing in a somatic therapy workbook also reflects an understanding of the central role that breath plays in our overall well-being and functioning. From a somatic perspective, the breath is seen not merely as a physiological process, but as a profound expression of our embodied state – a window into our deepest needs, fears, and desires. By learning to consciously engage and regulate the breath, we gain access to a powerful tool for self-awareness, self-expression, and self-transformation.

How to Use This Book

Introduction:

The introduction provides an overview of somatic therapy, its benefits, and the power of embodiment. It also includes essential information on safety and self-care, ensuring that you can engage with the content in a manner that feels supportive and nurturing.

Part I: Foundations of Somatic Therapy

In this section, you will learn about the fundamental concepts and principles that form the basis of somatic therapy. You will explore the mind-body connection, the role of the nervous system, and how trauma and stress affect the body. This section also includes exercises to help you develop body awareness and regulate your nervous system.

Part II: Developing Somatic Awareness

Building upon the foundations laid in Part I, this section focuses on cultivating somatic awareness through various practices and techniques. You will learn about mindfulness, interoception, presence, attunement, and breath regulation. Each chapter includes exercises to help you deepen your embodied experience and strengthen your connection with your body's signals and sensations.

Part III: Engaging with the Soma

In this section, you will explore ways to actively engage with your body and its wisdom. You will learn how to map your body's experiences, express yourself through movement, align with your authentic self, embody your boundaries, and work with body armor and chronic tension. The exercises in this section will help you develop a more intimate and compassionate relationship with your body.

Part IV: Somatic Tools for Stress and Trauma

This section provides a toolbox of somatic practices specifically designed to address stress and trauma. You will learn how to build a somatic resource toolkit, befriend your shame, navigate arousal and overwhelm, work with dissociation, and facilitate trauma healing through the body. The exercises in this section will help you develop resilience and the capacity to self-regulate in the face of challenging experiences.

Part V: Integration and Resilience

The final section of the workbook focuses on integrating the knowledge and skills you have acquired throughout the previous sections. You will learn how to cultivate radical self-compassion, engage in creativity and play, design a personalized somatic practice, and embody your resilience. The exercises in this section will help you sustain and deepen your somatic practice, fostering lasting growth and transformation.

To get the most out of this workbook, it is recommended that you work through the sections sequentially, as each one builds upon the previous. However, feel free to adapt the pace and focus to your individual needs and interests. The exercises and practices within each chapter are designed to be accessible and adaptable, allowing you to engage with them in a way that feels supportive and meaningful to you.

It is important to emphasize that somatic trauma work must be approached with great care and sensitivity. The pacing of the work should be adjusted to the individual's unique needs and capacity, ensuring that they are not re-traumatized in the process. This is why the section on working with trauma is placed at the end of the workbook. Before engaging with the practices and exercises in this section, it is crucial to have developed a solid foundation of embodied safety, resilience, and self-regulation.

The earlier sections of the workbook focus on cultivating somatic awareness, building resources, and developing the capacity for nervous system regulation. By first establishing these fundamental skills and capacities, individuals can create a stable and supportive container for the deeper, more intensive work of trauma processing.

It is recommended that individuals work through the preceding sections of the workbook at their own pace, taking the time to fully integrate and embody the practices and principles before moving on to the trauma-focused material. This gradual, incremental approach allows for a more organic and sustainable healing process, minimizing the risk of overwhelm or re-traumatization.

If, at any point during the exploration of the trauma section, individuals find themselves feeling dysregulated, dissociated, or triggered, it is important to pause, return to the foundational practices of grounding, resourcing, and self-care, and seek the support of a qualified therapist if needed. Remember, the path of trauma healing is not always linear, and it is essential to honor the wisdom and timing of your unique process.

By placing the trauma section at the end of the workbook, we aim to emphasize the importance of preparation, pacing, and self-compassion in the journey of somatic healing. With patience, practice, and the right support, it is possible to gradually and safely work through even the most challenging traumatic experiences, reclaiming a sense of wholeness, vitality, and connection to oneself and the world.

Common Terms in Somatics to Expand Your Understanding

CENTERING

Centering is the practice of bringing your awareness to the core of your being, the place of stillness and balance within. It involves grounding yourself in the present moment, aligning your physical, emotional, and mental state, and cultivating a sense of inner calm and stability. When we are centered, we are better able to navigate the challenges and uncertainties of life with grace, resilience, and clarity.

Centering can be achieved through various practices, such as deep breathing, meditation, yoga, or simply taking a moment to pause and connect with your inner landscape. By regularly returning to this place of equilibrium, we can develop a stronger sense of self, a more harmonious relationship with our environment, and a greater capacity for effective action and decision-making.

EMBODIMENT

Embodiment is the experience of fully inhabiting our physical form, of being deeply connected to and aware of the sensations, rhythms, and wisdom of our bodies. It is the recognition that our mind and body are not separate entities but rather an integrated whole, constantly influencing and informing each other.

When we are embodied, we are attuned to the subtle cues and signals of our somatic experience, such as our breath, heartbeat, muscle tension, and gut feelings. We can sense and respond to our needs and boundaries, communicate authentically and assertively, and move through the world with confidence and ease.

Cultivating embodiment is a central goal of somatic practices, which seek to bridge the gap between our conscious awareness and our unconscious, habitual patterns of holding and bracing. By learning to listen to and trust the intelligence of our bodies, we can access a deeper source of knowing, healing, and transformation.

MINDFULNESS

Mindfulness is the practice of bringing our attention to the present moment with openness, curiosity, and non-judgment. It involves observing our thoughts, feelings, and sensations as they arise without getting caught up in them or trying to change them.

Through mindfulness, we cultivate a greater awareness of our inner experience as well as the world around us. We learn to step back from our habitual reactions and impulses and to respond to life's challenges with greater clarity, compassion, and skill.

Mindfulness is a foundational element of many somatic practices, as it helps us to develop the capacity for embodied presence and self-reflection. By regularly tuning in to the here and now, we can interrupt patterns of stress, anxiety, and disconnection and cultivate a greater sense of peace, purpose, and well-being.

SOMA

Soma is a term derived from the Greek word for "body" and refers to the living, feeling, and sensing organism that we are. In somatic psychology, the soma is understood as the embodied self, the interwoven tapestry of our physical, emotional, and cognitive experience.

The soma is not just a passive vessel for the mind but a vibrant, intelligent system with its wisdom, memory, and agency. It is the source of our vitality, creativity, and intuition, as well as the storehouse of our unresolved wounds, traumas, and defenses.

SOMATICS

Somatics is an interdisciplinary field that encompasses a wide range of practices and approaches for cultivating embodied awareness, healing, and transformation. It includes modalities such as Somatic Experiencing, Sensorimotor Psychotherapy, Hakomi, Feldenkrais, and many others.

What unites these diverse practices is a shared understanding of the body as a vital source of intelligence, resilience, and change. Somatics recognize that our thoughts, beliefs, and histories shape our physical experience. By working directly with the body, we can access and transform the deep-rooted patterns that limit our potential.

STRESS RESPONSE

The stress response is a complex physiological reaction that occurs when we perceive a threat or challenge in our environment. It is orchestrated by the autonomic nervous system, which mobilizes the body's resources to deal with the stressor and restore homeostasis.

In the face of danger, the sympathetic nervous system activates the "fight, flight, or freeze" response, releasing hormones like adrenaline and cortisol to increase heart rate, blood pressure, and muscle tension. This prepares us to act and protect ourselves from harm.

Once the threat has passed, the parasympathetic nervous system initiates the "rest and digest" response, slowing down bodily functions and promoting relaxation and recovery.

While the stress response is a vital survival mechanism, chronic or excessive stress can take a toll on our physical and mental health, over time, constant activation of the stress response can lead to issues like anxiety, depression, insomnia, digestive problems, and weakened immunity.

PART I: FOUNDATIONS OF SOMATIC THERAPY

1. THE MIND-BODY CONNECTION

As we begin our exploration of somatic therapy, it is essential to establish a foundational understanding of the profound interconnectedness of our mental and physical experiences. For centuries, Western medicine and psychology have tended to view the mind and body as separate entities, each operating in isolation from the other. However, recent advances in neuroscience, psychophysiology, and other related fields have revealed a far more complex and intimate relationship between our thoughts, emotions, and physical sensations.

At the heart of this mind-body connection is the nervous system—the intricate network of neural pathways that serves as the communication highway between our brain and the rest of our body. From birth, our nervous system constantly receives and processes sensory information from our internal and external environments. This information is then translated into physiological responses, emotional states, and cognitive processes that shape our perception of ourselves and the world around us.

THE ROLE OF THE NERVOUS SYSTEM

It is helpful to have a basic overview of the nervous system's structure and function to understand how it mediates the mind-body connection. The nervous system is typically divided into two main branches: the central nervous system, which consists of the brain and spinal cord, and the peripheral nervous system, which includes all the nerves that extend throughout the body.

Within the peripheral nervous system, there are two further subdivisions: the somatic nervous system, which controls voluntary movements and receives sensory input from the skin, muscles, and joints, and the autonomic nervous system, which regulates involuntary functions such as heart rate, breathing, digestion, and sexual arousal. The autonomic nervous system is further divided into the sympathetic nervous system, which activates the "fight, flight, or freeze" response to stress or danger, and the parasympathetic nervous system, which promotes "rest and digest" functions and helps to calm the body down after a stressful event.

All these different branches and subdivisions of the nervous system work together in a complex and interconnected way to maintain homeostasis - the state of balanced, stable functioning that allows us to adapt to changing circumstances and demands. When we experience a stressful or threatening situation, for example, our sympathetic nervous system is activated, triggering a cascade of physiological changes such as increased heart rate, rapid breathing, and the release of stress hormones like cortisol and adrenaline. These changes help to mobilize our body's resources to deal with the perceived threat, whether that means fighting, fleeing, or freezing in place.

Once the threat has passed, our parasympathetic nervous system kicks in to help us recover and return to a state of relaxation and calm. This process of alternating between stress and relaxation is a natural and healthy part of our body's adaptive response to the world around us. However, when we experience chronic or overwhelming stress, our nervous system can become dysregulated, leading to a host of physical, emotional, and cognitive symptoms.

One of the key insights of somatic therapy is that our thoughts, emotions, and physical sensations are not separate or distinct experiences but various aspects of a single, integrated mind-body system. When we feel anxious or afraid, for example, we do not just experience those feelings in our mind - we also experience them in our body through sensations like tightness in the chest, tension in the shoulders, or butterflies in the stomach. Similarly, when we experience physical pain or discomfort, it can have a profound impact on our emotional state and thought patterns, leading to feelings of irritability, hopelessness, or despair.

This understanding of the mind-body connection is supported by neuroplasticity - the brain's ability to change and reorganize itself in response to new experiences and information. Research has shown that our thoughts, emotions, and behaviors can shape the structure and function of our brain over time, creating new neural pathways and patterns that influence our future experiences and responses. This means that, with the right tools and techniques, we can consciously reshape our mind-body system to promote greater health, resilience, and well-being.

HOW TRAUMA AND STRESS AFFECT THE BODY

One of the most profound examples of the mind-body connection can be seen in the way that trauma and chronic stress impact our physical health and functioning. When we experience a traumatic event - whether it is a single, overwhelming experience like a car accident or a prolonged period of abuse or neglect - our body's stress response system can become overactivated and dysregulated, leading to a host of physiological and psychological symptoms.

At a physiological level, trauma and chronic stress can lead to changes in the structure and function of our brain, particularly in areas involved in emotional regulation, memory, and threat perception. These changes can include hyperactivity in the amygdala, which participates in processing fear and anxiety, and reduced activity in the prefrontal cortex, which is responsible for higher-order thinking, decision-making, and impulse control.

Trauma and chronic stress can also profoundly impact our autonomic nervous system, leading to states of hyperarousal or hypoarousal that can persist long after the initial threat has passed. In a state of hyperarousal, our sympathetic nervous system becomes overactivated, leading to symptoms like increased heart rate, rapid breathing, and hypervigilance. This can make it difficult for us to relax, sleep, or engage in normal daily activities, as our body remains constantly alert.

In contrast, a state of hypoarousal occurs when our parasympathetic nervous system becomes dominant, leading to symptoms like fatigue, numbness, and disconnection from our body and emotions. This state of shutdown or collapse can be a way for our body to conserve energy and protect itself from further harm. Still, it can also leave us feeling trapped, helpless, and disconnected from our sense of agency and empowerment.

Another common response to trauma and chronic stress is dissociation - the experience of feeling disconnected or detached from our body, emotions, or surroundings. Dissociation can range from mild experiences of "spacing out" or daydreaming to more severe forms of depersonalization or derealization, where we feel like we are watching ourselves from outside our body or that the world around us is unreal or distorted.

While these different responses to trauma and stress can be adaptive in the short term, helping us to survive and cope with overwhelming experiences, they can also lead to long-term physical and psychological health problems if left unresolved.

EXERCISE: BODY AWARENESS JOURNALING

Body awareness journaling is a powerful practice for cultivating a deeper connection with your physical sensations, emotions, and overall embodied experience. By regularly taking time to tune in and record your somatic observations, you can develop greater self-awareness, self-compassion, and insight into your body's unique needs and patterns. This practice is an opportunity to create a safe, non-judgmental space for exploring and expressing your embodied truth and to track your growth and healing over time.

Guided Instructions

1. Begin by finding a quiet, comfortable space where you can write without interruption. Gather your journaling materials, such as a notebook and pen or a digital document, on your computer or device. Create a soothing and inviting atmosphere, perhaps by lighting a candle, playing soft music, or brewing a cup of tea.

2. Take a few slow, grounding breaths, allowing your body to settle and your mind to grow still. With each exhalation, release any tension or distractions and invite a sense of openness and curiosity.

3. When you feel ready, begin to tune into your body's sensations, starting with your breath. Notice the rhythm and depth of your inhalations and exhalations, as well as any areas of ease or constriction. Write down your observations without judgment, using descriptive language to capture the quality of your experience.

- ***Example:*** "My breath feels shallow and tight in my chest like I'm holding back. There's a sense of anxiousness fluttering in my belly."

4. Slowly guide your awareness through the various regions of your body, from your head to your toes. Notice any areas of tension, pain, numbness, or aliveness. Pay attention to subtle sensations like temperature, texture, and pressure. Record your observations in your journal, along with any associated emotions or thoughts that arise.

- ***Example:*** "My jaw feels clenched and tight like I'm gritting my teeth. I notice a sense of frustration and anger lodged there. My feet feel cold and disconnected, like I'm not fully grounded."

5. As you journal, try to stay present with your direct experience rather than getting caught up in analysis or interpretation. Use simple, straightforward language to describe your sensations, and avoid judging or criticizing your body's responses. If emotions or memories surface, acknowledge them with compassion and curiosity.

- ***Example:*** "There's a heavy sadness in my heart like a weight pressing down. I'm not sure where it's coming from, but I'm giving it space to be here."

6. In addition to recording challenges or discomforts, make sure to also note areas of ease, vitality, and pleasure in your body. Celebrate the moments of embodied joy, relaxation, or connection, no matter how small or fleeting. This helps to cultivate a balanced and appreciative relationship with your body.

- ***Example:*** "My hands feel warm and tingly like they're radiating energy. There's a sense of creativity and excitement buzzing in my fingertips."

7. As you complete your journaling session, take a moment to reread your observations with a sense of gentleness and acceptance. Offer gratitude to your body for its honesty and vulnerability and for all the ways it supports you each day. Set an intention to continue this practice regularly, even if just for a few minutes at a time.

Closing

Body awareness journaling is a simple yet profound way to deepen your relationship with your embodied self and cultivate greater self-awareness and self-compassion. By regularly taking time to tune in and record your somatic experiences, you create a valuable record of your growth and healing over time. Remember, your body's sensations and responses always communicate important information and guidance. By approaching them with curiosity, respect, and care, you open the door to greater wholeness, resilience, and embodied wisdom.

EXERCISE: EMBODIED CHECK-IN

The Embodied Check-In is a simple yet powerful exercise that helps you tune into your physical sensations, emotions, and thoughts, fostering a deeper connection between your mind and body. This practice can be done anywhere and at any time, making it a valuable tool for cultivating self-awareness and presence.

Steps

1. Find a comfortable seated or standing position, ensuring your spine is straight but not rigid. Close your eyes or maintain a soft, downward gaze.

2. Take a few deep breaths, allowing your body to settle and your mind to quieten. Notice the sensation of the breath moving in and out of your body.

3. Begin by bringing your attention to your feet. Notice the sensation of your feet making contact with the ground, the temperature, and any other sensations that arise. Take a moment to really feel your feet.

4. Slowly scan your attention up through your legs, noticing any sensations of tension, relaxation, warmth, coolness, tingling, or numbness. Don't try to change anything, simply observe what is present.

5. Continue scanning through your hips, lower back, stomach, and chest. Notice the rise and fall of your chest with each breath, as well as any sensations or emotions that are present in this area.

6. Bring your attention to your shoulders, arms, and hands. Notice if you are holding any tension here, and observe any other sensations that arise.

7. Scan up through your neck and throat, noticing if there is any tightness or constriction. Observe the sensations in your jaw, face, and head.

8. Take a moment to observe your entire body as a whole, noticing the overall sense of being embodied.

9. Now, turn your attention inwards to your emotional state. Notice what emotions are present for you in this moment without trying to change them or judge them. Simply acknowledge and name them.

10. Finally, observe your thoughts. Notice what thoughts are present in your mind, allowing them to come and go without getting attached to them.

11. Take a final few deep breaths, and when you feel ready, open your eyes and return your attention to your surroundings.

Closing

The Embodied Check-In was included in this book because it is a foundational practice for cultivating mind-body connection and self-awareness. By regularly checking in with your physical sensations, emotions, and thoughts, you can develop a deeper understanding of how your mind and body interact and learn to respond to your experiences with greater presence and compassion.

EXERCISE: MIND-BODY DIALOGUE

The Mind-Body Dialogue is a powerful exercise that helps to bridge the gap between our mental and physical experiences. By engaging in a written dialogue between the mind and body, we can gain insight into the relationship between our thoughts, emotions, and physical sensations. This exercise can help to cultivate greater self-awareness, self-compassion, and integration between the mind and body.

Steps

1. Find a quiet, comfortable space where you can write without interruption. Have a pen and paper or a journal ready.

2. Begin by taking a few deep breaths, allowing your body to settle and your mind to quieten. Close your eyes and take a moment to tune into your physical sensations and emotions.

3. Open your eyes and begin the dialogue by writing a question or statement from the perspective of your mind. This could be something like, "Hey body, how are you feeling today?" or "I've been feeling really stressed lately, and I'm not sure how it's affecting you."

4. Now, take a moment to tune into your body and imagine what your body might say in response. Write down the response from the perspective of your body. For example, "Dear mind, I'm feeling tired and tense. The stress you've been experiencing is showing up as tightness in the shoulders and a knot in the stomach."

5. Continue this back-and-forth dialogue between your mind and body, allowing each part to express itself freely. Some prompts you could use include:

- Mind: "What do you need from me right now?"
- Body: "I need you to take more breaks and move around more throughout the day."
- Mind: "I'm sorry I haven't been listening to you. What can I do to support you better?"
- Body: "Thank you for asking. I would appreciate more gentle stretching and some deep breathing exercises."

6. Allow the dialogue to unfold naturally, without judgment or censorship. If emotions arise, acknowledge them and allow them to be expressed through the writing.

7. When you feel the dialogue has come to a natural conclusion, take a moment to read back over what you've written. Notice any insights, themes, or areas for further exploration.

8. End the exercise by writing a brief reflection on what you've learned and any commitments you want to make to better support the relationship between your mind and body.

9. Close the exercise with a few deep breaths, and take a moment to appreciate the wisdom and insight that emerged from this dialogue.

Closing

The Mind-Body Dialogue exercise was included in this book because it is a powerful tool for cultivating self-awareness and integrating the often-disconnected aspects of our experience. By giving voice to both the mind and the body, we can develop a more compassionate and holistic understanding of ourselves, leading to greater well-being and self-care.

EXERCISE: MIND-BODY BALANCING ACT

The Mind-Body Balancing Act is an exercise designed to explore the interconnectedness of our mental and physical states. By engaging in a series of gentle movements and balance challenges, we can observe how our thoughts and emotions impact our physical stability and vice versa. This exercise helps to cultivate greater mind-body awareness, presence, and emotional regulation.

Steps

1. Find a quiet, open space where you can move freely without interruption. Ensure you have enough room to extend your arms and legs in all directions.

2. Begin by standing with your feet hip-width apart, finding a neutral and balanced stance. Take a few deep breaths, allowing your body to settle and your mind to become present.

3. Shift your weight onto your left foot and slowly lift your right foot off the ground. Notice any sensations of instability or wobbling, and observe any thoughts or emotions that arise.

4. Experiment with different arm positions, such as extending your arms out to the sides, overhead, or in front of your chest. Notice how each position affects your balance and your mental state.

5. If you feel stable, try closing your eyes while balancing on one foot. Notice how removing visual input changes your experience and challenges your balance in new ways.

6. When you're ready, lower your right foot back to the ground and take a moment to feel both feet connected to the earth. Notice any sensations of stability and groundedness.

7. Repeat the balancing exercise on the other side, lifting your left foot off the ground and exploring different arm positions and challenges.

8. After balancing on both sides, take a moment to reflect on your experience. Consider the following prompts:

- What thoughts or emotions arose during the balancing exercises?
- How did your mental state impact your physical balance?
- What did you notice about the relationship between stability and instability, both physically and mentally?

9. Experiment with other gentle movements or balance challenges, such as walking slowly and mindfully, or standing on a cushion or folded blanket. Continue to observe the interplay between your mind and body as you move.

10. End the exercise by returning to a neutral standing position, taking a few deep breaths, and acknowledging your experience.

Closing

The Mind-Body Balancing Act exercise was included in this book because it provides a simple yet profound way to explore the reciprocal relationship between our mental and physical states. By engaging in balance challenges and observing our experiences, we can develop greater mind-body awareness, emotional regulation, and presence. This exercise can be practiced regularly as a way to check in with ourselves and cultivate a more integrated sense of well-being.

2. REGULATING YOUR NERVOUS SYSTEM

As we deepen our understanding of the mind-body connection, we begin to recognize the vital role that our nervous system plays in shaping our moment-to-moment experience of life. Far from being a static or fixed system, our nervous system constantly responds and adapts to the changing demands of our internal and external environments. By learning to attune to and work with the subtle cues and signals of our nervous system, we can develop greater resilience, flexibility, and choice in how we navigate the difficulties of our embodied experience.

One of the most influential frameworks for understanding the functioning of the nervous system is the Polyvagal Theory, developed by Dr. Stephen Porges. According to this theory, our autonomic nervous system is not a simple binary system of "fight or flight" and "rest and digest" but rather a complex hierarchy of response states mediated by different branches of the vagus nerve, the longest and most complex of the cranial nerves.

UNDERSTANDING THE POLYVAGAL THEORY

At the top of this hierarchy is the ventral vagal complex, which is associated with feelings of safety, connection, and social engagement. When we are in a ventral vagal state, we feel calm, grounded, and open to the world around us. Our heart rate is stable, our breathing is deep and relaxed, and our facial expressions and vocal tones are warm and inviting. This is the state in which we are best able to learn, grow, and connect with others.

However, when we perceive a threat or challenge in our environment, our nervous system may shift into a sympathetic state, characterized by the classic "fight or flight" response. In this state, our heart rate increases, our breathing becomes rapid and shallow, and our muscles tense up in preparation for action. We may feel agitated, anxious, or angry, and our focus narrows to the immediate threat at hand.

If the sympathetic response is not sufficient to resolve the perceived threat, our nervous system may shift into a dorsal vagal state characterized by feelings of shutdown, collapse, or immobilization. In this state, our heart rate slows, our breathing becomes shallow and faint, and we may feel numb, disconnected, or "out of our body." This state is often associated with experiences of trauma or chronic stress, where the nervous system has become overloaded and is attempting to conserve energy and protect itself from further harm.

One of the key insights of Polyvagal Theory is that these different response states are not under our conscious control but rather are mediated by the autonomic nervous system in response to cues of safety or danger in our environment. This means that we may find ourselves shifting between different states throughout the day, often without even realizing it.

THE WINDOW OF TOLERANCE

To understand how dysregulation occurs, it is helpful to introduce the concept of the "window of tolerance," developed by Dr. Dan Siegel. The window of tolerance refers to the optimal zone of nervous system arousal in which we can process and integrate our experiences healthily and adaptively.

When we are within our window of tolerance, we feel relatively calm, grounded, and able to engage with the world around us. We think clearly, communicate effectively, and respond flexibly to changing circumstances and demands. This is the state in which we are best able to learn, grow, and connect with others.

However, when we experience stress or trauma that pushes us outside of our window of tolerance, we may find ourselves in a state of either hyperarousal or hypoarousal. In a state of hyperarousal, we may feel agitated, anxious, or overwhelmed, with racing thoughts, tense muscles, and a sense of being "on edge." In a state of hypo arousal, we may feel numb, disconnected, or "shut down," with a sense of heaviness, fatigue, and lack of motivation.

These states of hyperarousal and hypo arousal are not inherently "bad" or "negative" but rather are the body's way of trying to cope with overwhelming stress or trauma. However, when we get stuck in these states for prolonged periods, they can start to interfere with our ability to function and thrive.

One of the goals of somatic therapy is to help individuals expand their window of tolerance, develop a greater capacity to regulate their nervous system, and stay grounded and present in the face of stress and challenge. This involves learning to recognize the subtle cues and signals of hyperarousal and hypo arousal in the body and developing tools and strategies for shifting back towards a state of ventral vagal connection and engagement.

Some common signs of hyperarousal include rapid, shallow breathing, tense muscles, racing heartbeat, feeling "on edge" or unable to relax, difficulty sleeping, irritability or anger, and difficulty concentrating. Signs of hypoarousal include slow, shallow breathing, feeling heavy or fatigued, numbness or disconnection from the body and emotions, difficulty focusing, feelings of hopelessness, lack of motivation, and difficulty connecting with others.

By learning to recognize these signs and symptoms in ourselves, we can start to develop greater awareness of our nervous system's response patterns and triggers. We can also reframe these states as adaptive biological responses that are trying to help us cope with overwhelming stress or trauma.

EXERCISE: TRACKING YOUR NERVOUS SYSTEM

Tracking your nervous system is a foundational practice in somatic awareness and regulation. By learning to identify and differentiate the various states of your autonomic nervous system—such as sympathetic activation, dorsal vagal shutdown, or ventral vagal safety—you can develop a greater capacity for self-awareness, self-regulation, and resilience. This practice involves tuning into the subtle signs and sensations that indicate which branch of your nervous system is currently dominant and learning to gently guide yourself towards a more regulated and resourced state.

Guided Instructions

1. Begin by finding a quiet, comfortable space where you can sit or lie down without interruption. Take a few slow, deep breaths, allowing your body to settle and your mind to grow still. With each exhalation, release any tension or distractions and invite a sense of openness and curiosity.

2. Start by checking in with your overall sense of safety and connection. Do you feel relatively calm, grounded, and present? Or do you notice sensations of anxiety, overwhelm, or disconnect? Acknowledge your current state without judgment.

3. Now, bring your attention to your physical sensations, starting with your breath. Notice the rhythm and depth of your inhalations and exhalations. Is your breath rapid and shallow, or slow and deep? Does it feel constricted or expansive? These qualities can give you clues about your nervous system state.

- **Example:** Rapid, shallow breathing may indicate sympathetic activation (fight or flight), while slow, deep breathing may suggest ventral vagal engagement (safety and connection).

4. Next, scan your body for other indicators of your nervous system state. Check in with your muscle tension, heart rate, temperature, and digestion. Are your muscles tense and contracted, or soft and relaxed? Is your heartbeat fast and pounding, or slow and steady? Do you feel warm and flushed or cold and clammy? Is your digestion moving smoothly, or do you feel constipated or have diarrhea?

- **Example:** Tight muscles, racing heart, and feeling hot may point to sympathetic activation. Feeling cold, numb, and shut down may indicate dorsal vagal collapse. A relaxed body, steady heartbeat, and good digestion often signify ventral vagal safety.

5. In addition to physical cues, tune into your emotional and mental state. Are you feeling anxious, irritable, or restless? Do you feel disconnected, hopeless, or numb? Or do you feel relatively calm, engaged, and clear-minded? These experiences can also reflect your underlying nervous system activation.

- **Example:** Anxiety, anger, and racing thoughts often accompany sympathetic arousal. Feeling dissociated, depressed, and mentally foggy may suggest a dorsal vagal shutdown. A sense of centeredness, curiosity, and engagement often comes with ventral vagal safety.

6. As you identify your current nervous system state, see if you can bring an attitude of acceptance and compassion to your experience. Remember that these states are not always within your conscious control and that they serve an important protective function. Avoid judging or criticizing yourself for being in a particular state.

7. If you notice signs of sympathetic or dorsal vagal activation, explore ways to gently guide your nervous system toward a more regulated and resourced state. This might involve slowing down your breath, orienting yourself to your environment, engaging in gentle movement, or reaching out for support. The goal is not to force a change but to invite a gradual shift towards greater safety and connection.

- **Example:** If you are feeling anxious and agitated, try taking a few deep, slow breaths while placing a hand on your belly. Look around your space and name a few objects you see. Remind yourself that you are safe at this moment.

8. With regular practice, you can develop a more nuanced and responsive relationship with your nervous system, learning to track its subtle cues and support its natural regulatory capacity. Remember to approach this practice with patience, curiosity, and self-compassion, trusting your body's innate wisdom and resilience.

Closing

Tracking your nervous system is a powerful tool for cultivating embodied self-awareness and self-regulation. By learning to identify and respond to the subtle signs of your autonomic states, you can develop a greater sense of agency, resilience, and adaptability in navigating life's challenges. Remember, your nervous system is constantly working to protect and support you, even when its responses feel uncomfortable or overwhelming. By approaching it with respect, compassion, and care, you can gradually build a sense of safety and trust within yourself and deepen your capacity for connection and engagement with the world around you. May this practice be a source of insight, nourishment, and empowerment on your ongoing journey of growth and healing.

EXERCISE: EXPANDING YOUR WINDOW OF TOLERANCE

Your window of tolerance refers to the range of emotional and physiological arousal that you can comfortably tolerate and function within. When you are within your window of tolerance, you feel relatively grounded, resourced, and able to respond flexibly to life's challenges. However, when you are outside your window of tolerance—either hyper-aroused or hypo-aroused—you may feel overwhelmed, reactive, or shut down. This practice is designed to help you gradually expand your window of tolerance so that you can navigate a wider range of experiences with greater ease and resilience.

Guided Instructions

1. Begin by finding a quiet, comfortable space where you can sit or lie down without interruption. Take a few slow, deep breaths, allowing your body to settle and your mind to grow still. With each exhalation, release any tension or distractions and invite a sense of openness and curiosity.

2. Start by tuning into your current level of arousal. Notice any physical sensations, emotions, or thoughts that are present. Are you feeling relatively calm and centered, or do you notice signs of hyper-arousal (such as racing thoughts, anxiety, or agitation) or hypo-arousal (such as numbness, disconnection, or fatigue)? Acknowledge your current state without judgment.

3. Now, recall a mildly challenging or activating situation from your recent past. This should be something that feels slightly outside your window of tolerance but not overwhelmingly so. It might be a difficult conversation, a stressful work deadline, or a minor conflict with a loved one.

4. As you bring this situation to mind, notice how your body responds. What sensations, emotions, or impulses arise? Do you feel your heartbeat quickening, your muscles tensing, or your breath becoming shallow? Or do you feel a sense of heaviness, numbness, or collapse? Stay with these sensations for a few moments, allowing them to be present without getting lost in the story or the details of the situation.

5. Now, see if you can bring a small amount of relaxation or ease to your experience. This might involve taking a few slow, deep breaths, softening any areas of tension in your body, or recalling a soothing image or resourceful memory. The goal is not to eliminate the activation but to introduce a bit of regulation and support.

6. As you work with this mildly challenging situation, notice if you can stay present and engaged without becoming overwhelmed or shutting down. Can you maintain a sense of grounding and perspective even as you feel the edges of your window of tolerance? If you find yourself getting dysregulated, take a break and return to your resources and grounding practices.

7. With regular practice, you can gradually work with more intense or prolonged situations, building your capacity to tolerate and regulate a wider range of experiences. The key is to go slowly, respect your limits, and prioritize your safety and well-being.

8. In addition to working with specific situations, you can also explore practices that help to build your overall resilience and regulatory capacity. This might include regular meditation or breathwork, engaging in physical exercise or creative expression, spending time in nature, or connecting with supportive others.

Closing

Expanding your window of tolerance is a gradual, ongoing process that requires patience, self-compassion, and a willingness to work with discomfort. By regularly engaging in practices that help you regulate your nervous system and build your resilience, you can develop a greater capacity to navigate life's difficulties with ease and adaptability. Remember, your window of tolerance is not fixed or static but can shift and grow over time with intentional practice and support. May this practice be a source of empowerment, self-discovery, and healing on your journey toward greater wholeness and well-being.

EXERCISE: POLYVAGAL-INFORMED BREATHING

Polyvagal-Informed Breathing is an exercise that utilizes diaphragmatic breathing techniques and an understanding of the polyvagal theory to help regulate the nervous system. By focusing on deep, slow breaths and visualizing a sense of safety and connection, this exercise aims to engage the ventral vagal complex, promoting a state of calm and social engagement. Regularly practicing this technique can help individuals develop greater resilience and emotional regulation skills.

Steps

1. Find a comfortable seated position, either on a chair with your feet flat on the ground or cross-legged on a cushion. Ensure your spine is straight but not rigid and your shoulders are relaxed.

2. Gently close your eyes or maintain a soft, downward gaze. Take a moment to settle into your body and notice any physical sensations or emotions that are present.

3. Place one hand on your chest and the other on your belly. Take a slow, deep breath in through your nose, focusing on expanding your belly as you inhale. Notice the sensation of your hand rising with your belly.

4. Exhale slowly through your mouth, allowing your belly to fall and your hand to lower. Imagine any tension or stress leaving your body with each exhalation.

5. Continue this deep, diaphragmatic breathing pattern, inhaling through your nose and exhaling through your mouth. Aim for a slow, steady rhythm of about 5-6 breaths per minute.

6. As you breathe, visualize a sense of safety and connection. This might involve picturing a loved one, a favorite place in nature, or a comforting memory. Focus on the feelings of warmth, comfort, and security that arise with this visualization.

7. If your mind begins to wander or you notice any feelings of anxiety or discomfort, gently redirect your attention back to your breath and the sensations of safety and connection.

8. Continue this deep breathing and visualization practice for 5-10 minutes or for as long as it feels comfortable for you.

9. When you're ready to conclude the practice, take a final few deep breaths and gently open your eyes, allowing yourself to reorient to your surroundings.

10. Take a moment to notice any shifts in your physical sensations, emotions, or overall sense of well-being. Acknowledge the practice of self-care and nervous system regulation.

Closing

Polyvagal-Informed Breathing was included in this book because it offers a simple yet powerful tool for regulating the nervous system and promoting a sense of calm and safety. By combining diaphragmatic breathing with an understanding of the polyvagal theory and visualizations of connection, this exercise helps individuals to engage their ventral vagal complex and shift into a more regulated state. With regular practice, Polyvagal-Informed Breathing can be a valuable addition to any self-care or stress-management toolkit.

EXERCISE: PMR FOR NERVOUS SYSTEM REGULATION

Progressive Muscle Relaxation (PMR) is a technique that involves systematically tensing and relaxing different muscle groups in the body to promote deep relaxation and nervous system regulation. By actively tensing and then releasing muscle groups, we can help to release chronic tension, reduce stress and anxiety, and promote a sense of calm and well-being. This exercise is particularly useful for down-regulating the nervous system from a state of hyperarousal or stress response.

Steps

1. Find a quiet, comfortable place where you can lie down or sit in a supportive chair. Ensure you won't be disturbed for the duration of the practice.

2. Begin by taking a few deep breaths, allowing your body to settle and your mind to become present. Notice any existing areas of tension or discomfort without judgment.

3. Starting with your feet and toes, take a deep breath in and actively tense the muscles in this area, scrunching your toes and contracting your feet. Hold the tension for 5-7 seconds, noticing the sensation of tightness and contraction.

4. Exhale slowly and release the tension in your feet and toes, allowing them to relax completely. Notice the sensation of release and relaxation, and take a moment to appreciate the difference between tension and relaxation.

5. Move your attention up to your lower legs and calves. Inhale deeply and tense the muscles in this area, squeezing your calves and lifting your heels off the ground. Hold the tension for 5-7 seconds.

6. Exhale and release the tension in your lower legs and calves, allowing them to relax fully. Again, notice the sensation of release and relaxation.

7. Continue this pattern of tensing and relaxing each muscle group, moving up through your body. Focus on the following areas:

- Thighs and buttocks
- Hips and pelvis
- Stomach and lower back
- Chest and upper back
- Shoulders and neck
- Arms and hands
- Face (forehead, eyes, cheeks, mouth, and jaw)

8. For each muscle group, remember to inhale and tense for 5-7 seconds, then exhale and release, noticing the contrast between tension and relaxation.

9. After completing the sequence, take a few deep breaths and scan your body for any remaining areas of tension. If you notice any residual tightness, repeat the tensing and relaxing process for that specific area.

10. Finally, imagine a wave of relaxation flowing through your entire body from head to toe, allowing yourself to sink into a deep state of relaxation and calm.

11. When you feel ready, gently wiggle your fingers and toes and slowly open your eyes, taking a moment to reorient to your surroundings.

Conclusion

Progressive Muscle Relaxation for Nervous System Regulation was included in this book because it is a highly effective technique for down-regulating the nervous system and promoting a state of deep relaxation. By actively tensing and releasing different muscle groups, we can help to release chronic tension, reduce stress and anxiety, and cultivate a greater sense of mind-body awareness. With regular practice, PMR can be a powerful tool for enhancing resilience, emotional regulation, and overall well-being.

EXERCISE: COHERENT BREATHING WITH HRVB

Coherent Breathing with Heart Rate Variability Biofeedback (HRVB) is an exercise that combines the practice of slow, rhythmic breathing with the use of biofeedback technology to help regulate the nervous system, reduce stress, and promote a sense of well-being. By breathing at a rate of around 5-6 breaths per minute, which is often referred to as the "resonant frequency," we can optimize our heart rate variability and cultivate a state of physiological coherence. The use of HRVB technology helps to provide real-time feedback on our breathing patterns and heart rate variability, making it easier to find and maintain our resonant frequency.

Steps

1. Begin by finding a comfortable seated position, either on a chair or on the ground. Ensure your spine is straight but not rigid and your shoulders are relaxed. You may choose to close your eyes or keep them softly focused on a point in front of you.

2. Attach the HRVB device according to the manufacturer's instructions. This may involve placing a finger clip or ear sensor or attaching electrodes to your chest.

3. Take a few deep breaths, allowing your body to settle and your mind to become present. Notice any physical sensations, emotions, or thoughts that arise without judgment.

4. Start by breathing at your normal pace observing your heart rate variability on the HRVB device. Notice any patterns or fluctuations in your heart rate.

5. Gradually slow your breathing down, aiming for a rate of around 5-6 breaths per minute. This typically involves inhaling for a count of 5-6 seconds and exhaling for a count of 5-6 seconds. The HRVB device may provide visual or auditory cues to help guide your breathing pace.

6. As you continue to breathe at this slower pace, notice any changes in your heart rate variability pattern. Look for signs of increased coherence, such as a smooth, sine-wave-like pattern on the HRVB display.

7. If you find it challenging to maintain this slower breathing pace, try imagining your breath moving in and out like gentle ocean waves or visualize a peaceful scene in nature that matches your breathing rhythm.

8. Continue coherent breathing with the HRVB device for 5-10 minutes or for as long as it feels comfortable for you. If your mind begins to wander or you notice any feelings of strain or discomfort, gently redirect your attention back to your breath and the biofeedback display.

9. When you're ready to conclude the practice, take a final few deep breaths and gently open your eyes, allowing yourself to reorient to your surroundings.

10. Remove the HRVB device and take a moment to notice any shifts in your physical sensations,

emotions, or overall sense of well-being. Acknowledge the practice of self-care and nervous system regulation.

Conclusion

Coherent Breathing with HRVB was included in this book because it offers a powerful tool for regulating the nervous system, reducing stress, and promoting a sense of physiological coherence. By combining the practice of slow, rhythmic breathing with the use of biofeedback technology, this exercise helps individuals to find and maintain their resonant frequency, optimizing heart rate variability and cultivating a state of calm and well-being. With regular practice, Coherent Breathing with HRVB can be a valuable addition to any stress-management or self-care toolkit, helping to build resilience and emotional balance over time.

EXERCISE: HEART-FOCUSED BREATHING WITH HRVB

Heart-Focused Breathing with Heart Rate Variability Biofeedback (HRVB) is an exercise that combines the practice of slow, deep breathing with a focus on positive emotions and the use of biofeedback technology to help regulate the nervous system, reduce stress, and promote a sense of emotional well-being. By breathing deeply and directing our attention to the area of the heart while cultivating feelings of appreciation, gratitude, or compassion, we can shift our physiological state and increase heart rate variability coherence. The use of HRVB technology helps to provide real-time feedback on our breathing pattern, heart rate variability, and emotional state, making it easier to achieve and sustain a state of coherence.

Steps

1. Begin by finding a comfortable seated position, either on a chair or on the ground. Ensure your spine is straight but not rigid and your shoulders are relaxed. You may choose to close your eyes or keep them softly focused on a point in front of you.

2. Attach the HRVB device according to the manufacturer's instructions. This may involve placing a finger clip or ear sensor or attaching electrodes to your chest.

3. Take a few deep breaths, allowing your body to settle and your mind to become present. Notice any physical sensations, emotions, or thoughts that arise without judgment.

4. Bring your attention to the area around your heart. You may choose to place one or both hands over your heart center to help focus your awareness.

5. Begin to breathe deeply and rhythmically, imagining your breath flowing in and out through your heart area. Inhale for a count of 5-6 seconds, and exhale for a count of 5-6 seconds, finding a comfortable, smooth rhythm.

6. As you continue to breathe deeply, bring to mind a positive feeling or emotional state, such as

appreciation, gratitude, or compassion. You may choose to focus on a specific person, place, or experience that evokes these feelings.

7. With each inhalation, imagine breathing in the positive feeling or emotion, allowing it to fill your heart and expand throughout your body. With each exhalation, imagine radiating that positive energy outward to yourself and others.

8. As you sustain this heart-focused breathing and positive emotional state, observe your heart rate variability pattern on the HRVB device. Notice any shifts towards increased coherence, such as a smooth, sine-wave-like pattern.

9. If your mind begins to wander or you notice any feelings of strain or discomfort, gently redirect your attention back to your breath, your heart center, and the positive emotional focus.

10. Continue the Heart-Focused Breathing with HRVB exercise for 5-10 minutes or for as long as it feels comfortable for you.

11. When you're ready to conclude the practice, take a final few deep breaths and gently open your eyes, allowing yourself to reorient to your surroundings.

12. Remove the HRVB device and take a moment to notice any shifts in your physical sensations, emotions, or overall sense of well-being. Acknowledge the practice of self-care, emotional regulation, and cultivating positive states.

Conclusion

Heart-Focused Breathing with HRVB was included in this book because it offers a powerful tool for regulating the nervous system, reducing stress, and promoting emotional well-being. By combining deep, rhythmic breathing with a focus on positive emotions and the use of biofeedback technology, this exercise helps individuals achieve and sustain a state of physiological and emotional coherence. With regular practice, Heart-Focused Breathing with HRVB can be a valuable addition to any emotional self-regulation or stress-management toolkit, helping to build resilience, positive emotional states, and overall well-being over time.

PART II: DEVELOPING SOMATIC AWARENESS

3. MINDFULNESS AND BODY AWARENESS

As we begin our exploration of somatic awareness, it is essential to understand the foundational role that mindfulness plays in this process. Mindfulness is often defined as the practice of bringing non-judgmental attention to the present moment with openness, curiosity, and acceptance. While mindfulness is commonly associated with sitting meditation and other formal practices, it can also be applied to every aspect of our lived experience, including our embodied sensations, emotions, and perceptions.

In the context of somatic therapy, we often speak of "embodied mindfulness" as a way of distinguishing this body-centered approach from more cognitive or conceptual forms of mindfulness. Embodied mindfulness involves bringing our attention specifically to the felt sense of our bodily experience in the present moment, with a spirit of gentle inquiry and self-compassion.

This might involve noticing the subtle sensations of our breath moving in and out of our body, the weight of our feet on the ground, or the texture of our clothing on our skin. It might also involve tuning into the physical sensations that accompany our emotions, such as the tightness in our chest when we feel anxious or the warmth in our belly when we feel content.

The key to embodied mindfulness is not to analyze or judge these sensations but to observe them with kind and curious attention. By learning to be present with our body in this way, we can start to develop a deeper and more nuanced understanding of our inner landscape and cultivate greater self-awareness, self-regulation, and self-compassion.

One of the primary benefits of embodied mindfulness is that it helps us to develop a greater capacity for self-regulation. When we are disconnected from our body and its sensations, we are more likely to get caught up in reactive patterns of thought and behavior, such as rumination, avoidance, or impulsivity. These patterns can lead to a sense of being out of control or at the mercy of our emotions and can contribute to feelings of anxiety, depression, or stress.

By contrast, when we can stay present with our bodily experience mindfully and compassionately, we can start to notice the early warning signs of dysregulation, such as shallow breathing, muscle tension, or a racing heartbeat. We can then use this awareness to make more conscious and intentional choices about how to respond to our experience rather than getting swept away by our automatic reactions.

Another key benefit of embodied mindfulness is that it can help us to develop greater somatic insight

47

and self-understanding. When we are disconnected from our bodies, we may struggle to make sense of our thoughts, feelings, and behaviors or to understand the deeper patterns and beliefs that drive them. We may feel like we are living at the surface level of our experience without access to the rich and complex world that lies beneath.

By contrast, when we bring mindful attention to our bodily sensations and experiences, we can start to uncover the hidden wisdom and intelligence of our somatic self. We may notice patterns of tension or holding in our body that reflect unresolved emotional wounds or traumas. We may discover subtle sensations or impulses that point us toward new possibilities for growth and healing. We may even experience moments of profound insight or revelation as we connect with the deeper truths and meanings of our embodied experience.

Of course, cultivating embodied mindfulness is not always easy or comfortable. It requires a willingness to be present with our discomfort, vulnerability, and uncertainty and to meet ourselves with compassion and patience. It also requires a certain level of discipline and commitment as we learn to prioritize our somatic awareness in the midst of our busy and distracting lives.

However, the rewards of this practice are immeasurable. As we deepen our embodied mindfulness, we may find that we are able to navigate the challenges and complexities of life with greater ease, resilience, and grace. We may discover new sources of creativity, vitality, and joy as we learn to trust and follow the wisdom of our body. And we may even experience a profound sense of connection and belonging as we recognize our fundamental interconnectedness with all of life.

You might start by setting aside a few minutes each day to tune into your bodily sensations without any agenda or expectation. You might notice the feeling of your breath moving in and out of your body, the sensations of your hands or feet, or the subtle shifts in your posture and muscle tone. You might also experiment with different postures or movements, such as stretching, walking, or dancing, and notice how these activities affect your embodied experience.

EXERCISE: BODY SCAN MEDITATION

The body scan meditation is a foundational mindfulness practice that involves systematically bringing attention to different parts of the body, from the toes to the crown of the head. This practice helps to cultivate present-moment awareness, release tension and stress, and deepen your connection with your physical sensations and overall embodied experience. By regularly engaging in body scan meditation, you can develop greater self-awareness, self-compassion, and a sense of wholeness and integration within yourself.

Guided Instructions
1. Begin by finding a quiet, comfortable space where you can lie down or sit without interruption. If lying down, choose a firm, supportive surface such as a yoga mat or a carpeted floor. If sitting, ensure that your spine is upright and your feet are firmly planted on the ground.

2. Take a few slow, deep breaths, allowing your body to settle and your mind to grow still. With each exhalation, release any tension or distractions and invite a sense of openness and curiosity.

3. Gently close your eyes or soften your gaze towards the floor. Bring your attention to your breath, noticing the natural inhalation and exhalation without trying to control or change it. Observe the breath as it moves in and out of your body.

4. Now, shift your attention to your left toes. Notice any sensations that are present, such as warmth, coolness, tingling, or pressure. If you do not feel anything, that is okay too. Just notice the absence of sensation. Take a few breaths, imagining that you are breathing in and out of your toes.

5. Slowly move your attention up to your left foot, ankle, and lower leg. Again, notice any sensations that are present without judging or analyzing them. If your mind wanders, gently bring it back to the part of the body you are focusing on.

6. Continue this process, moving your attention gradually up your left leg to your hip and then starting again with your right toes. Move slowly and systematically, taking your time to really feel and experience each part of your body.

7. When you have scanned both legs, bring your attention to your pelvic area, noticing any sensations in your hips, buttocks, and lower back. Then, move up to your abdomen, chest, and upper back, observing the rise and fall of your breath.

8. Scan your hands, arms, and shoulders, noticing any areas of tension or holding. Invite those areas to soften and release, as if you are gently melting any tightness or constriction.

9. Finally, bring your attention to your neck, face, and head. Notice your jaw, your mouth, your eyes, and your forehead. See if you can bring a sense of softness and ease to these areas, letting go of any tension or holding.

10. When you have completed the body scan, take a few deep breaths and notice how your body feels as a whole. Observe any shifts or changes in your physical sensations, emotions, or overall state of being.

11. Gently wiggle your fingers and toes, and slowly open your eyes. Take a moment to reorient yourself to your surroundings, bringing your awareness back to the present moment.

Closing

The body scan meditation is a powerful tool for cultivating embodied mindfulness and self-awareness. By regularly practicing this technique, you can learn to tune into your body's subtle sensations, release tension and stress, and develop a greater sense of presence and integration within yourself. Remember, the goal is not to force relaxation or achieve a particular state but to observe and be with your experience as it unfolds. With time and practice, the body scan can become a deeply nourishing and transformative practice, supporting your overall health, well-being, and personal growth.

EXERCISE: MINDFUL MOVEMENT

Mindful movement is a practice that combines gentle physical movements with present-moment awareness and breath. This practice can help to release tension, improve flexibility and balance, and cultivate a deeper sense of connection between the mind and body. By bringing mindfulness to our movements, we can develop greater self-awareness, self-compassion, and a sense of embodied presence. Mindful movement can be practiced through various forms, such as yoga, tai chi, or qigong, or through simple, everyday movements done with intentional awareness.

Guided Instructions

1. Begin by finding a quiet, comfortable space where you can stand or sit without interruption. Take a few slow, deep breaths, allowing your body to settle and your mind to grow still. With each exhalation, release any tension or distractions and invite a sense of openness and curiosity.

2. Start by bringing your attention to your body, noticing the sensation of your feet on the ground or your sit bones on the chair. Feel the connection between your body and the surface beneath you, allowing yourself to feel grounded and supported.

3. Gently lift your arms overhead, inhaling as you reach up. As you exhale, slowly lower your arms back down to your sides. Repeat this movement a few times, synchronizing your breath with the motion of your arms. Notice the stretch and release in your shoulders, chest, and upper back.

4. Next, bring your attention to your neck and head. Gently drop your right ear towards your right shoulder, feeling a stretch along the left side of your neck. Take a few breaths here, then slowly lift your head back to the center. Repeat on the other side, dropping your left ear towards your left shoulder.

5. Now, shift your attention to your spine. Slowly roll your shoulders back and down, feeling your shoulder blades drawing together and your chest opening. Then, gently round your spine forward, tucking your chin towards your chest and feeling a stretch in your upper back. Alternate between these two movements, inhaling as you open your chest and exhaling as you round your spine.

6. If you are standing, take a few slow, mindful steps in place. Feel the sensation of your feet contacting the ground, noticing the shift of weight from one foot to the other. If you are sitting, gently rock your hips from side to side, feeling the movement in your pelvis and lower back.

7. Continue to explore gentle, mindful movements that feel good for your body. You might try stretching your arms out to the sides, making slow circles with your wrists or ankles, or gently twisting your torso from side to side. The key is to move slowly and with intention, staying present with the sensations and experiences that arise.

8. As you move, notice any thoughts or emotions that come up. Observe them with curiosity and without judgment, allowing them to pass through your awareness like clouds in the sky. If your mind wanders, gently bring it back to the present moment, anchoring your attention in your breath and

physical sensations.

9. When you feel ready to close the practice, take a few deep breaths and notice how your body feels. Observe any shifts or changes in your physical sensations, emotions, or overall state of being.

Closing

Mindful movement is a powerful way to cultivate embodied presence, self-awareness, and self-compassion. By bringing mindfulness to our physical experiences, we can learn to release tension, improve our overall well-being, and deepen our connection with ourselves and the world around us. Remember, the goal is not to achieve a particular outcome or state but to be present and curious with your experience as it unfolds. With regular practice, mindful movement can become a nurturing and transformative part of your self-care routine, supporting your physical, emotional, and spiritual growth.

EXERCISE: SENSORY GROUNDING TECHNIQUES

Sensory grounding techniques are simple yet powerful tools for bringing awareness back to the present moment and regulating the nervous system. These techniques involve intentionally focusing on one or more of the five senses—sight, sound, touch, smell, and taste—to anchor oneself in the here and now. Grounding techniques can be particularly helpful during times of stress, anxiety, or overwhelm, as they help to shift attention away from distressing thoughts or emotions and into the concrete, tangible reality of the present. With regular practice, sensory grounding can become a reliable resource for self-regulation and resilience.

Guided Instructions

1. Begin by finding a comfortable seated position, either on a chair or on the floor. Take a few slow, deep breaths, allowing your body to settle and your mind to grow still. If you feel comfortable doing so, gently close your eyes to minimize visual distractions.

2. Start by bringing your attention to your sense of touch. Notice the sensation of your body making contact with the surface beneath you—the pressure of your sit bones on the chair or cushion, the texture of your clothing against your skin. Take a few breaths, really focusing on these tactile sensations.

3. Next, if you have a small object nearby (such as a smooth stone, a soft fabric, or a textured toy), pick it up and explore it with your hands. Notice the object's temperature, weight, and texture. Is it warm or cool to the touch? Is it heavy or light in your hand? Does it have any bumps, ridges, or patterns? Take your time, letting your fingers explore the object with curiosity and openness.

4. Now, shift your attention to your sense of hearing. Notice any sounds that are present in your environment, both near and far. You might hear the hum of appliances, the rustle of leaves outside, or the distant sound of traffic. See if you can identify three different sounds, focusing on each one for a

few breaths.

5. If you have a pleasant scent available (such as an essential oil, a scented candle, or a fragrant herb), bring it close to your nose and take a few gentle inhales. Notice how the scent affects your body and mind. Does it evoke any emotions or memories? Does it help you feel more calm, alert, or grounded?

6. Finally, bring your awareness to your sense of taste. If you have a small piece of food or drink available (such as a mint, a slice of fruit, or a sip of tea), take a moment to savor it slowly. Notice the sensations of taste, texture, and temperature in your mouth. See if you can identify different flavors or qualities, such as sweet, salty, sour, or bitter.

7. After you have explored each sense individually, take a few moments to expand your awareness to all of your senses simultaneously. Notice how your body feels with all its sensory input and experience. Take a few deep breaths, feeling your feet on the ground and your body supported by the surface beneath you.

8. When you are ready, gently open your eyes and take a moment to reorient yourself to your surroundings. Notice any shifts in your energy, mood, or state of mind. See if you can carry this sense of grounded, sensory awareness with you as you move through the rest of your day.

Closing

Sensory grounding techniques are a simple yet effective way to bring ourselves back to the present moment and regulate our nervous system. By intentionally focusing on our sensory experience, we can interrupt cycles of worry, stress, or distress and cultivate a greater sense of presence and resilience. Remember, grounding techniques are most effective when practiced regularly, even when you are not feeling particularly anxious or overwhelmed. By incorporating sensory awareness into your daily routine, you can build a solid foundation of self-regulation and inner stability. Trust that with each practice, you are strengthening your capacity to meet life's challenges with greater ease, groundedness, and grace.

4. THE ROLE OF INTEROCEPTION

As we deepen our exploration of somatic awareness, it is essential to understand the crucial role that interoception plays in this process. Interoception refers to our ability to sense and perceive the internal states and signals of our body, such as our heartbeat, breathing, hunger, thirst, temperature, and emotional sensations. It is the foundation of our embodied self-awareness and plays a vital role in our physical, emotional, and cognitive functioning.

UNDERSTANDING INTEROCEPTION

At its core, interoception is about tuning into the subtle language of our body and learning to decipher the messages and meanings that it is constantly communicating to us. Unlike our external senses, such as sight or hearing, which are focused on perceiving the world around us, interoception is concerned with the inner landscape of our bodily experience.

This inner landscape is incredibly rich and complex, encompassing a wide range of sensations, impulses, and feelings that are constantly arising and passing away within us. From the rhythmic pulsing of our heartbeat to the churning of our digestive system, from the tingling of our skin to the aching of our muscles, our body is always speaking to us, offering a wealth of information about our physical, emotional, and mental states.

However, for many of us, this inner language can be difficult to understand or even to notice, as we have become disconnected from our bodily experience through years of stress, trauma, or cultural conditioning. We may have learned to ignore or override the signals of our body, pushing ourselves beyond our limits or numbing ourselves to our own needs and desires.

The good news is that interoceptive abilities can be cultivated and strengthened through practice, just like any other skill or capacity. By learning to tune into the subtle sensations and signals of our body with curiosity, compassion, and presence, we can start to develop a deeper and more nuanced understanding of our own embodied experience.

This process of interoceptive attunement is not about trying to control or manipulate our bodily states but rather about learning to listen and respond to them with greater wisdom and care. As we become more skilled at sensing and interpreting our body language, we can start to make more informed and compassionate choices about how to care for ourselves, both physically and emotionally.

Through this process of interoceptive inquiry, we can start to develop a more intimate and trusting relationship with our own embodied experience and access the deep well of wisdom and intelligence that resides within us. We can learn to navigate the difficulties of life with greater resilience, adaptability, and grace, knowing that we have the inner resources and guidance to support us along the way.

EXERCISE: TUNING INTO YOUR BODY'S SIGNALS

This practice builds interoceptive awareness - our ability to sense and interpret internal bodily cues. Interoceptive awareness underlies emotional intelligence, self-regulation, and mind-body integration. While everyone has some innate capacity for interoception, this exercise enhances that ability.

The goal is to systematically practice turning inward to sense the physical signals that often go unnoticed. This enhances interoceptive abilities that allow deeper embodied experiencing and regulation of emotional and physiological states. The more we attune to these signals, the more empowered our mind-body integration becomes.

Approach this practice with a gentle, non-judging attitude of curiosity. Remember, there is no right or wrong way to experience your bodily sensations; allow yourself to be present with whatever arises.

Preparing Your Practice Space

Find a comfortable position, either seated or lying down. Ensure you are in a space where you feel safe and at ease. If you would like, have a journal and pen nearby to record any observations or insights that may emerge.

Take a moment to remove any potential distractions from your environment, such as silencing your phone or closing your computer. If it helps you relax, feel free to play soft, atmospheric soundscapes in the background.

Guided Instructions

1. Begin by taking a few calming breaths to settle into your body. Close your eyes if that feels comfortable, and bring your awareness to the physical sensations of breathing.

2. Notice the gentle rise and fall of your abdomen, the cool air entering your nostrils, and the warm air leaving your body.

3. Now, systematically tune into different bodily signals, lingering with open awareness on each domain for 1-2 minutes. If your mind wanders, gently acknowledge the thoughts and return your attention to the specified area.

- **Heartbeat:** Place your hand over your heart and feel its steady rhythm. Notice the subtle pulsations that reverberate through your chest.
- **Breath:** Bring your awareness back to your breath. Observe the expansion of your ribcage as you inhale and the release as you exhale. Pay attention to the subtle pauses between each breath.
- **Sounds:** Tune into any internal sounds within your body. You might notice a gentle rumbling in your stomach, the whooshing of blood through your veins, or a subtle ringing in your ears.
- **Skin Sensations:** Shift your focus to your skin. Notice any tingling, temperature changes, or the texture of your clothing against your body. Observe any areas of your skin that feel particularly alive or numb.

- **Muscles:** Bring your awareness to your muscles. Scan your body from head to toe, detecting any areas of tension, tightness, or ease. Notice how your muscles respond to your breath and any subtle shifts in position.

Reflective Inquiry

As you complete the body scan, take a moment to reflect on your experience:

- Were there any signals that were easier or harder for you to sense?
- How did your emotional state influence what you felt in your body?
- Did you gain any new insights into your mind-body connections?

Consider setting an intention to continue tuning into these bodily signals regularly. The more you practice interoceptive awareness, the more empowered you become in understanding and regulating your emotional and physiological states.

Closing

To close the practice, take a few final grounding breaths. Slowly begin to reorient your surroundings, wiggling your fingers and toes and gently opening your eyes when you feel ready.

If you would like, take a moment to write down any reflections or insights that arose during the practice. Remember, cultivating interoceptive awareness is a journey, and each experience offers valuable wisdom.

Through regular practice, you will develop a deeper attunement to the subtle language of your body, fostering a greater sense of embodiment, emotional resilience, and mind-body integration. Trust in the wisdom of your body and the power of your presence.

THE CONNECTION BETWEEN INTEROCEPTION AND EMOTION

One of the most important aspects of interoception is its close relationship with our emotional experience. Emotions are not just mental states or cognitive appraisals but are fundamentally embodied and visceral experiences that are felt and expressed through the body.

When we experience an emotion, such as fear, anger, or joy, our body undergoes a complex series of physiological changes that are designed to prepare us for action and to communicate our inner state to others. Our heart rate may increase, our breathing may become rapid and shallow, our muscles may tense up, and our facial expressions and body language may shift to reflect our emotional state.

These bodily changes are not random or arbitrary. Still, they are part of a highly orchestrated response that is mediated by the autonomic nervous system and other regulatory processes in the brain and body. Each emotion has its unique pattern of physiological activation and expression, which can be felt and sensed through the lens of interoceptive awareness.

By tuning into these subtle somatic cues, we can start to develop a more nuanced and embodied understanding of our emotional landscape. We can learn to recognize the early warning signs of emotional dysregulation, such as a sense of agitation or disconnection, and to respond with greater skill and care.

This process of interoceptive attunement is particularly important for regulating intense or difficult emotions, such as anxiety, grief, or shame. When we are caught in the grip of these emotions, it can be easy to get overwhelmed or reactive, losing touch with our inner wisdom and resilience.

However, by learning to stay present and grounded in our bodily experience, even during intense emotional states, we can start to develop a greater capacity for self-regulation and emotional intelligence. We can learn to ride the waves of our emotions with greater ease and skill, knowing that they are temporary and changeable and that we have the inner resources to navigate them with compassion and wisdom.

Through this process of interoceptive attunement, we can start to develop a more flexible and adaptive relationship with our emotions, recognizing them as valuable sources of information and guidance rather than as threats or obstacles to be avoided or suppressed. We can learn to trust in our own embodied wisdom and resilience, knowing that we can meet whatever arises with presence, compassion, and skill.

EXERCISE: MAPPING YOUR INTEROCEPTIVE LANDSCAPE

In this practice, we will be exploring the geography of inner bodily sensations. The goal is to develop a rich, nuanced awareness of our interoceptive experience. By mapping our internal landscape, we can cultivate a deeper relationship with our embodied selves.

Remember, there is no right or wrong way to engage in this practice - just an open, nonjudgmental observation of your unique somatic terrain. Trust your intuition and let curiosity guide the mapping process.

Preparing Your Practice Space

Find a comfortable position, either seated or lying down. Have a notepad and colored pencils or markers ready. If it helps you focus inward, you may choose to play soft ambient music in the background. You may also want to set a timer for 20-30 minutes to allow yourself ample time for this self-reflective practice.

Guided Instructions

1. Begin by taking a few calming breaths, allowing your awareness to settle into your body. Notice the overall landscape of bodily sensations—the textures, temperatures, and rhythms that arise.

2. Now, choose a specific area of your body to zoom in on, such as your hands, feet, or abdomen. Let your attention gently land here.

3. Adopt an open, quasi-meditative awareness, observing the sensations in this area without analyzing or judging. Be present with what is.

4. Notice any subtle pulsations, shifting, or fluid movements within this body part. You might feel the delicate pulse of blood pumping, the slight expansion and contraction with each breath, or the brief tingling of energy.

5. Allow yourself to be captivated by these micro-movements, observing them with a childlike sense of wonder. Notice their rhythm, texture, and aliveness.

6. When you feel ready, slowly shift your micro-attention to another area of your body. Again, tune into the nuanced dance of sensations happening just beneath the surface.

Mapping Your Experience

1. Now, let us begin to map out these interoceptive experiences. You can make an abstract body map or depict specific sensations through individual doodles or symbols. Use colors, words, or whatever experimental modes feel expressive to you.

2. For each area you tuned into, get imaginative - what images, shapes, colors, and metaphors capture the felt sense? For example, a tight knot in the belly could be sketched as a tangled ball of yarn.

3. Let it be a free-flowing, spontaneous process. The key is bringing a beginner's mind to the task of describing your interoceptive experience.

4. Work slowly through different areas, tracking the shifting qualities of sensation with your sketches and jottings. Let it be a playful, intuitive process rather than an analytical one.

5. Once you have spent sufficient time mapping, take a pause and notice if your overall body sense has shifted from this focused attunement.

Closing

Take a moment to witness and appreciate this somatic self-portrait you have created. Offer gratitude for the wisdom and aliveness contained within your inner sensory landscape.

This interoceptive mapping is an evolving, iterative process. You can return to and add to this map anytime, letting it be a living document of your embodied experiences.

Through regular practice, this type of somatic mapping enhances our capacity for interoceptive awareness, emotional granularity, and self-intimacy. It is a powerful tool for cultivating embodied insight and transformation.

Trust in the intelligence of your body and the revelations that emerge through this process of inner listening and creative expression. May this practice deepen your self-understanding and attunement and enliven your mind-body relationship.

EXERCISE: INTEROCEPTIVE PROGRESSIVE MUSCLE RELAXATION

Interoceptive Progressive Muscle Relaxation is a powerful exercise that combines the techniques of progressive muscle relaxation (PMR) with interoceptive awareness. This practice involves systematically tensing and relaxing different muscle groups while focusing on the accompanying physical sensations, such as warmth, heaviness, or tingling. By bringing mindful attention to these interoceptive cues, you can deepen your awareness of the body's internal states and cultivate a greater sense of mind-body connection. This exercise can be helpful for reducing stress, improving sleep, and promoting overall relaxation and well-being.

Steps

1. Find a quiet, comfortable place where you can sit or lie down without disturbance. If sitting, ensure your feet are flat on the ground, and your hands are resting comfortably on your lap. If lying down, allow your arms to rest by your sides, with your palms facing up.

2. Close your eyes and take a few deep breaths, allowing your body to settle and your mind to become present. Notice any existing sensations, thoughts, or emotions without judgment.

3. Begin by focusing your attention on your feet and toes. Tense the muscles in this area by curling your toes and clenching your feet, holding the tension for 5-7 seconds. As you do so, notice the sensations of tightness and contraction.

4. Now, exhale and release the tension, allowing your feet and toes to relax completely. As you do so, pay close attention to the physical sensations associated with relaxation, such as warmth, heaviness, or tingling. Take a moment to fully experience these interoceptive cues.

5. Move your attention to your lower legs and calves. Tense these muscles by pointing your toes toward your head and lifting your legs slightly off the ground. Hold the tension for 5-7 seconds, noticing the sensations of tightness and contraction.

6. Exhale and release the tension, allowing your lower legs and calves to relax completely. Again, focus on the physical sensations of relaxation, such as warmth or heaviness, and take a moment to fully experience these interoceptive cues.

7. Continue this process of tensing, noticing, relaxing, and sensing with each muscle group, moving up through your body in the following order:

- Thighs and buttocks
- Hips and pelvis
- Stomach and lower back
- Chest and upper back
- Shoulders and neck
- Arms and hands
- Face (forehead, eyes, cheeks, mouth, and jaw)

8. For each muscle group, remember to tense for 5-7 seconds, noticing the sensations of tension, then release and focus on the interoceptive cues associated with relaxation.

9. After completing the sequence, take a few deep breaths and scan your body for any remaining areas of tension. If you notice any residual tightness, repeat the tensing and relaxing process for that specific area, with a focus on the interoceptive sensations.

10. Finally, imagine a wave of relaxation and warmth flowing through your entire body, from the top of your head to the tips of your toes. Allow yourself to rest in this state of deep relaxation and interoceptive awareness for a few moments.

11. When you feel ready, gently wiggle your fingers and toes and slowly open your eyes, taking a moment to reorient to your surroundings.

Conclusion

Interoceptive Progressive Muscle Relaxation was included in this book because it offers a powerful way to combine the benefits of progressive muscle relaxation with the cultivation of interoceptive awareness. By systematically tensing and relaxing different muscle groups while focusing on the accompanying physical sensations, you can develop a deeper understanding of your body's internal states and promote a greater sense of mind-body integration. Regular practice of this exercise can help to reduce stress, improve sleep, and enhance overall well-being by strengthening the connection between your conscious mind and your body's inner wisdom.

EXERCISE: INTEROCEPTIVE BREATHING AND APPLIED RELAXATION

Interoceptive Breathing and Applied Relaxation is an exercise that combines deep, diaphragmatic breathing with relaxation techniques to enhance interoceptive awareness and promote a state of calm and well-being. By focusing on the internal sensations associated with the breath and applying relaxation techniques to different areas of the body, you can cultivate a deeper sense of mind-body connection and develop skills for self-regulation and stress management. This exercise can be particularly helpful in moments of anxiety, tension, or overwhelm, providing a grounding and centering practice to return to a state of balance and ease.

Steps

1. Find a quiet, comfortable place where you can sit or lie down without disturbance. If sitting, ensure your feet are flat on the ground, and your hands are resting comfortably on your lap. If lying down, allow your arms to rest by your sides, with your palms facing up.

2. Close your eyes and take a few deep breaths, allowing your body to settle and your mind to become present. Notice any existing sensations, thoughts, or emotions without judgment.

3. Place one hand on your chest and the other on your belly. Begin to focus on your breath, noticing the sensation of the air moving in and out of your nostrils and the rise and fall of your chest and belly with each inhalation and exhalation.

4. As you continue to breathe, bring your attention to the internal sensations associated with your breath. Notice the coolness of the air as you inhale and the warmth as you exhale. Observe any sensations of expansion or contraction in your chest and belly, as well as any subtle vibrations or pulsations in your body as you breathe.

5. Now, begin to apply relaxation techniques to different areas of your body, starting with your feet and moving up toward your head. As you focus on each area, imagine the breath flowing into that part of the body, bringing with it a sense of relaxation and ease.

6. For example, as you focus on your feet, imagine the breath moving down through your legs and into your feet, allowing them to relax and soften. You might visualize the breath as a warm, soothing light or a gentle wave washing over your feet and carrying away any tension or discomfort.

7. Continue this process of breathing into and relaxing each part of your body, moving through your legs, hips, lower back, stomach, chest, upper back, shoulders, arms, hands, neck, face, and head. Take your time with each area, allowing yourself to fully experience the sensations of relaxation and release.

8. If you notice any areas of particular tension or discomfort, you can spend a bit more time breathing into those areas, imagining the breath gently dissolving any tightness or constriction.

9. Once you've completed the relaxation process, take a few deep breaths and observe your entire body as a whole. Notice the overall sense of calm, presence, and interoceptive awareness that you've cultivated.

10. Gently open your eyes and take a moment to reorient to your surroundings, carrying this sense of relaxation and interoceptive connection with you as you continue your day.

Conclusion

Interoceptive Breathing and Applied Relaxation was included in this book because it offers a simple yet effective way to cultivate interoceptive awareness, promote relaxation, and develop skills for self-regulation. By combining deep, diaphragmatic breathing with applied relaxation techniques, you can create a powerful mind-body practice that can be used in moments of stress, anxiety, or tension. Regular practice of this exercise can help you to better understand and regulate your internal states, ultimately promoting greater emotional well-being, resilience, and overall health.

5. CULTIVATING PRESENCE AND ATTUNEMENT

As we continue our exploration of somatic awareness, it is important to understand the essential role that presence and attunement play in this process. Presence refers to the quality of being fully engaged and awake to our moment-to-moment experience without distraction or resistance. Attunement, on the other hand, refers to the capacity to sense and respond to the subtle cues and signals of our own embodied experience, as well as the experiences of others around us.

Together, presence and attunement form the foundation of a deep and nourishing relationship with us and the world around us. They allow us to move beyond the surface level of our experience and to access the rich and complex landscape of sensation, emotion, and meaning that lies beneath.

EXPLORING SENSATIONS IN THE BODY

One of the key practices for cultivating presence and attunement is the exploration of sensations in the body. This practice involves moving beyond our habitual ways of thinking about or analyzing our bodily experience and instead allowing ourselves to directly feel and sense the raw data of our embodied awareness.

When we first begin this practice, it can be helpful to start with the simple act of noticing the sensations of our breath. We might bring our attention to the feeling of the air moving in and out of our nostrils, the expansion and contraction of our chest and belly, or the subtle vibrations of our breath in our throat or sinuses.

As we deepen our awareness of these sensations, we may start to notice more subtle qualities and textures of our breathing, such as the temperature of the air, the moisture or dryness of our breath, or the rhythmic pulsing of our heartbeat underlying the flow of our inhalations and exhalations.

From this foundation of breath awareness, we can start to expand our attention to other areas of our body, exploring the diverse landscape of sensation that is always present, whether we are aware of it or not. We might notice the weight and pressure of our body against the surface beneath us, the tension or relaxation in our muscles, or the tingling and pulsing of our blood moving through our veins.

As we continue this exploration, we may start to discover a whole universe of sensory experiences that we have never noticed before. We might sense the subtle vibrations of our organs working inside of us, the electric buzz of our nervous system firing, or the shimmering field of energy that surrounds and permeates our body.

We may also start to notice the constant stream of micro-movements and shifts that are happening within us all the time, from the flickering of our eyelids to the swaying of our spine with each breath.

These movements may be so small and subtle that we have never paid attention to them before. Still, they are a vital part of our embodied experience, reflecting the dynamic and ever-changing nature of our being.

This practice of pure sensing can be challenging at first, as our minds are so used to being in charge and making meaning out of everything we experience. We may find ourselves getting distracted by thoughts, memories, or judgments or feeling frustrated when we do not immediately understand what we are sensing.

EXERCISE: SENSORY AWARENESS PRACTICE

This practice is designed to cultivate embodied presence by immersing yourself in pure somatic awareness. The intention is to allow sensations to arise without analysis, bringing gentle, open attention to your inner experience.

Guided Instructions

1. Find a comfortable position, either seated or lying down. Ensure your posture is stable and relaxed, allowing for easy breathing.

2. Begin by taking a few slow, deep breaths. With each exhalation, feel your body settling more deeply into stillness.

3. Anchor your attention inwardly by focusing on the physical sensations of breathing. Notice the air moving in and out, the gentle rise and fall of your chest and belly.

4. Expand your awareness to encompass your entire body. Without narrating or analyzing, notice the panoramic field of sensations arising within you.

5. Allow your awareness to move through your body, scanning from head to toe. Meet each sensation with open curiosity, without the need to label or interpret.

6. Tune into the subtle nuances of your somatic experience. Notice temperatures, textures, vibrations, and micro-movements. Be present with the ever-shifting landscape of sensations.

7. Periodically, incorporate other sense experiences into your awareness. Listen to the sounds around you, noticing tones, pitches, and rhythms. Attend to any scents or tastes that arise, observing how they resonate in your body.

8. Bring a sense of childlike innocence to your sensing process. Allow yourself to be immersed in the raw sensory experience without the need to narrate or analyze.

9. If desired, integrate gentle, mindful movements into your practice. Slowly stretch or shift your body, maintaining a seamless connection with your inner sensations.

10. Throughout the practice, if your mind wanders into thinking, gently guide your attention back to your direct sensory experience.

Closing

To conclude, take a few final grounding breaths. Offer a moment of gratitude for your capacity to cultivate embodied awareness. Slowly reorient yourself to your surroundings, carrying this quality of presence with you as you transition back into your day.

DEVELOPING DUAL AWARENESS

Another key practice for cultivating presence and attunement is the development of dual awareness. Dual awareness refers to the capacity to maintain a simultaneous awareness of our inner, somatic experience and our outer, environmental experience without getting lost in either one.

In our daily lives, we often tend to focus either on our internal world of thoughts, feelings, and sensations or on the external world of people, places, and things around us. We may get so caught up in our own mental chatter or emotional reactions that we lose touch with what is happening in the present moment, or we may get so focused on the tasks and demands of the external world that we neglect our own inner needs and experiences.

Dual awareness, on the other hand, involves learning to balance and integrate these two modes of being so that we can be fully present and attuned to both our inner and outer worlds at the same time. This practice involves cultivating a kind of open, spacious awareness that can hold both our somatic experience and our cognitive understanding without getting trapped in either one.

One way to practice dual awareness is through the simple act of noticing. This involves bringing gentle, curious attention to whatever is arising in our experience, whether it is a sensation in our body, a thought in our mind, or a sound in the environment around us. We are not trying to analyze or judge what we are noticing but simply allowing it to be there without getting caught up in it or pushing it away.

As we practice this kind of open, undistracted noticing, we may start to discover a greater sense of spaciousness and ease in our experience. We may find that we are able to be present with both our inner and outer worlds without feeling overwhelmed or disconnected from either one.

We may also start to notice the ways in which our somatic experience and our cognitive understanding are constantly influencing and informing each other. For example, we may notice how a particular thought or belief can create a corresponding sensation in our body or how a bodily experience can shift our mental and emotional state.

Through this practice of dual awareness, we can start to develop a more integrated and holistic understanding of ourselves and the world around us. We can learn to navigate the complexities of our experience with greater skill and flexibility, knowing that we can be present and attuned to whatever arises, whether it is pleasant or unpleasant, familiar or unfamiliar.

Of course, developing dual awareness is not always easy, and it requires a certain level of discipline and commitment. We may find ourselves getting easily distracted or overwhelmed by the intensity of our experience or feeling like we are constantly struggling to maintain a balance between our inner and outer worlds.

EXERCISE: EMBODIED PRESENCE PRACTICE

By immersing yourself in pure sensory awareness without analysis, you can access a profound state of inner stillness and connection. Approach this practice with a gentle, allowing attitude as you tune inward.

Guided Instructions

1. Begin by finding a comfortable position, either seated or lying down. Ensure your posture is relaxed yet alert, allowing for easy, natural breathing.

2. Take a few slow, deep breaths, letting each exhalation soften your body more deeply into a state of restful awareness.

3. Anchor your attention inwardly by focusing on the subtle sensations of breathing. Notice the cool air entering your nostrils, the gentle expansion of your chest, and the soft release as you exhale.

4. Expand your awareness to encompass your entire body, as if you are listening to the symphony of sensations arising within you. Without narrating or analyzing, observe the panoramic field of your somatic experience.

5. Allow your awareness to gently move through your body, scanning from head to toe. Meet each sensation with open, nonjudgmental curiosity without the need to label or interpret.

6. Tune into the subtle nuances of your inner landscape. Notice the interplay of temperatures, textures, vibrations, and micro-movements. Be present with the ever-shifting tapestry of sensations.

7. Periodically, incorporate other sense experiences into your awareness. Listen to the soundscape around you, attending to the quality of silence beneath the sounds. Observe any scents or tastes that arise, feeling how they resonate in your body.

8. Bring a sense of childlike wonder to your sensing process. Allow yourself to be immersed in the raw, immediate experience of each sensation without the need to narrate or analyze.

9. If desired, integrate gentle, mindful movements into your practice. Slowly stretch or shift your body, maintaining a seamless connection with your inner sensations. Move from a place of embodied

listening, honoring your body's natural impulses.

10. Throughout the practice, if your mind wanders into thought, gently guide your attention back to the anchor of your breath and the immediacy of your sensory experience.

Closing
To conclude, take a few final grounding breaths, savoring the quality of embodied presence you have cultivated. As you slowly reorient yourself to your surroundings, carry this sense of inner connection and attunement with you, infusing your day with greater mindfulness and ease.

EXERCISE: SENSORY MODULATION

Sensory modulation involves adjusting our sensory input to help regulate our nervous system's arousal levels. By learning to skillfully use different sensory techniques, we can help our body and mind achieve an optimal "window of tolerance" - a state of calm-focused attunement.

Some sensory inputs can be soothing and grounding when we feel hyper-aroused or anxious, while others can be stimulating and energizing when we feel hypo-aroused or lethargic. Experiment with these different techniques to discover what works best for your unique sensory system.

Guided Instructions
1. Begin by tuning into your current state of arousal or depletion. Notice any sensations of restlessness, agitation, or anxiety that might indicate hyper-arousal. Or observe any feelings of fatigue, spaciness, or low motivation that could point to hypo-arousal.

2. If you are feeling hyper-aroused or overstimulated, try one or more of these calming techniques:

- Apply deep pressure touch to your body through self-massage, hugging, or wrapping yourself tightly in a blanket. The weight and compression can help you feel more grounded and contained.
- Engage in slow, rhythmic movements like rocking, swaying, or gentle stretching. These repetitive motions can be soothing to the nervous system and help discharge excess energy.
- Use your voice to hum, chant, or sing in a low, calming tone. The vibrations and resonance can promote a sense of internal stability and regulation.
- Focus on regulating your breath by slowing down the inhale and elongating the exhale. You can count your breaths or use phrases like "in" and "out" to help maintain a steady, grounding rhythm.

3. If you are feeling hypo-aroused or under-responsive, try one or more of these stimulating techniques:

- Engage in brisk, invigorating movements like jumping jacks, high knees, or shaking out your limbs. These exercises can boost your energy and alertness.
- Listen to upbeat, energizing music that makes you want to move and engage with your surroundings. The rhythm and tempo can help shift your nervous system into a more active state.
- Smell strong, stimulating scents like citrus, peppermint, or rosemary. These aromas can be awakening and help clear any mental fog or dullness.
- Eat or drink something with a crunchy, chewy, or sour texture, like a crisp apple, a piece of gum, or a tart beverage. The intense sensations can help stimulate your senses and boost your focus.

4. Remember that sensory modulation is a highly individual process, so what works for one person may not work for another. Be open to experimenting with different techniques and pay attention to how your body and mind respond. Over time, you can develop a personalized "sensory diet" that helps you regulate your arousal levels throughout the day.

Closing

Sensory modulation is a powerful tool for self-regulation and nervous system balance. By learning to attune to our arousal states and respond with appropriate sensory inputs, we can cultivate greater resilience, adaptability, and well-being.

Consider integrating regular "sensory check-ins" into your daily routine, taking brief pauses to assess your arousal and engage in modulating practices as needed. Over time, this can help you build a more flexible, resilient nervous system that can navigate a range of experiences with greater ease.

EXERCISE: ATTUNED BREATHING AND PROGRESSIVE MUSCLE RELAXATION

Attuned Breathing and Progressive Muscle Relaxation is an exercise that combines two powerful relaxation techniques to promote deep relaxation, reduce stress and anxiety, and cultivate a greater sense of mind-body awareness. By synchronizing your breath with gentle muscle relaxation, you can create a profound sense of calm and release tension throughout your entire body. This exercise is particularly helpful for those who experience chronic stress, muscle tension, or difficulty sleeping, as it helps to promote a state of deep rest and relaxation.

Steps

1. Find a quiet, comfortable place where you can lie down or sit comfortably without disturbance. If lying down, use a yoga mat or blanket for support, and allow your arms to rest by your sides with your palms facing up. If sitting, ensure your feet are flat on the ground, and your hands are resting comfortably on your lap.

2. Close your eyes and take a few deep breaths, allowing your body to settle and your mind to become

present. Notice any areas of tension or discomfort in your body without judgment.

3. Begin by focusing on your breath, noticing the natural flow of inhalation and exhalation. Slowly deepen your breath, allowing your belly to expand with each inhalation and fall with each exhalation. Continue this deep, diaphragmatic breathing throughout the exercise.

4. As you continue to breathe deeply, bring your attention to your feet and toes. On your next exhalation, gently squeeze your feet and toes as if you were trying to grip the floor with them. Hold this tension for a few seconds, noticing the sensation of tightness and contraction.

5. On your next inhalation, release the tension in your feet and toes, allowing them to relax completely. Notice the sensation of release and letting go, and feel the wave of relaxation spreading through your feet and toes.

6. Move your attention to your lower legs and calves. As you exhale, gently flex your feet and point your toes towards your face, engaging your calf muscles. Hold this tension for a few seconds, synchronizing it with your breath.

7. On your next inhalation, release the tension in your calves, allowing your feet to return to a neutral position. Feel the wave of relaxation spreading through your lower legs, releasing any remaining tension or tightness.

8. Continue this process of tensing and relaxing each muscle group in synchrony with your breath, moving progressively up through your body. Follow this sequence:

- Thighs and buttocks
- Hips and pelvis
- Stomach and lower back
- Chest and upper back
- Shoulders and neck
- Arms and hands
- Face (forehead, eyes, cheeks, mouth, and jaw)

9. For each muscle group, remember to tense on the exhalation, hold for a few seconds, and then release and relax on the inhalation. Take your time and move slowly, allowing yourself to fully experience the sensations of tension and relaxation in each area.

10. After completing the sequence, take a few deep breaths and scan your entire body for any remaining areas of tension. If you notice any residual tightness, gently direct your breath to those areas and invite them to relax.

11. Finally, allow yourself to rest in this state of deep relaxation for a few moments, enjoying the sense of calm and ease that you've cultivated. When you feel ready, gently wiggle your fingers and toes and slowly open your eyes, taking a moment to reorient to your surroundings.

Conclusion

Attuned Breathing and Progressive Muscle Relaxation was included in this book because it offers a highly effective way to reduce stress, release muscle tension, and promote deep relaxation. By combining the power of diaphragmatic breathing with systematic muscle relaxation, this exercise helps to cultivate a profound sense of mind-body awareness and balance. Regular practice of this technique can lead to improved sleep, reduced anxiety, and a greater overall sense of well-being and resilience.

EXERCISE: MINDFUL ATTUNEMENT AND HEART RATE VARIABILITY BIOFEEDBACK

Mindful Attunement and Heart Rate Variability Biofeedback is an exercise that combines mindfulness practices with biofeedback technology to help you cultivate emotional balance, self-regulation, and a deep sense of mind-body connection. Heart Rate Variability (HRV) is a measure of the variation in time between consecutive heartbeats, which reflects the health and resilience of your autonomic nervous system. By focusing on positive emotions while monitoring your HRV, you can learn to intentionally shift your physiological state towards greater coherence and well-being. This exercise is particularly helpful for those who experience chronic stress, anxiety, or emotional dysregulation.

Steps

1. Begin by setting up your HRV biofeedback device according to the manufacturer's instructions. This may involve attaching sensors to your ear, finger, or chest and connecting the device to a computer or mobile app.

2. Find a quiet, comfortable place where you can sit without disturbance. Sit in a chair with your feet flat on the ground and your hands resting comfortably on your lap.

3. Close your eyes and take a few deep breaths, allowing your body to settle and your mind to become present. Notice any existing sensations, thoughts, or emotions without judgment.

4. Start the HRV biofeedback session on your device and observe your HRV data as it begins to display on the screen. Most devices will show a graph of your heart rate over time, along with various metrics such as your HRV score or coherence level.

5. As you continue to breathe normally, bring to mind a positive emotion or experience that evokes feelings of love, gratitude, appreciation, or compassion. This could be a cherished memory, a beloved person or pet, or a sense of connection to nature or something greater than yourself.

6. Allow yourself to fully immerse in this positive emotional state, noticing any sensations of warmth, openness, or expansiveness in your body. You may place a hand on your heart center to deepen your connection with these feelings.

7. As you sustain this positive focus, observe your HRV data on the screen. Notice if your HRV increases or becomes more coherent with a smooth, sine-wave-like pattern. This is a sign that your nervous system is shifting into a state of greater balance and resilience.

8. If your mind begins to wander or you notice any feelings of stress or tension, gently redirect your attention back to your breath and your chosen positive emotion. You may also try synchronizing your breath with your heartbeat, inhaling for a count of 4-6 heartbeats and exhaling for the same count.

9. Continue the exercise for 10-20 minutes or for as long as it feels comfortable for you. Allow yourself to rest in this state of mindful attunement and physiological coherence, savoring the feelings of well-being and connection.

10. When you're ready to conclude the exercise, take a few deep breaths and gently open your eyes, taking a moment to reorient to your surroundings. Notice any shifts in your emotional state or overall sense of well-being.

11. Reflect on your experience and consider how you might integrate this practice of mindful attunement and positive emotional focus into your daily life, particularly during times of stress or challenge.

Conclusion

Mindful Attunement and Heart Rate Variability Biofeedback was included in this book because it offers a powerful way to cultivate emotional balance, self-regulation, and resilience. By combining mindfulness practices with biofeedback technology, you can learn to intentionally shift your physiological state towards greater coherence and well-being, even in the face of stress or adversity. Regular practice of this exercise can help you develop a deeper sense of mind-body connection, improve your ability to manage difficult emotions and promote overall health and happiness.

6. BREATH AWARENESS AND REGULATION

In the realm of somatic therapy, breath holds a special place as one of the most powerful and accessible tools for cultivating embodied presence, emotional regulation, and deep healing. Our breath is with us from the moment we are born until the moment we die, a constant companion on the journey of life. By learning to bring conscious awareness and intention to this often-overlooked aspect of our being, we open a doorway to profound transformation and resilience.

THE IMPORTANCE OF BREATH IN SOMATIC THERAPY

At its core, the breath is a potent anchor to the present-moment experience of embodiment. With each inhalation and exhalation, we are invited to arrive fully in the here and now to feel the subtle sensations and rhythms of our body. Unlike many other physiological processes that happen automatically and unconsciously, breath is unique in that it can be both involuntary and voluntary. We can allow our breathing to unfold naturally in the background of our awareness, or we can choose to bring it into the foreground, shaping its depth, pace, and quality.

This capacity for conscious breathing holds immense potential for somatic healing and growth. By tuning into our breath with curiosity and care, we can begin to explore the intimate relationship between our breathing patterns and our emotional states. We may notice how, in moments of stress, anxiety, or fear, our breath becomes shallow and constricted, trapped in the upper chest. In contrast, when we feel safe, relaxed, and content, our breath tends to be deeper, slower, and more expansive, originating from the belly.

These observations point to a profound truth: our breath is a mirror of our inner world. The way we breathe both reflects and affects our emotional landscape. When we are caught in the grip of intense or overwhelming emotions, our breathing patterns can become dysregulated, perpetuating cycles of tension, reactivity, and distress. However, by learning to work consciously with our breath, we can harness its power to regulate our nervous system, process difficult experiences, and cultivate greater emotional resilience.

DIAPHRAGMATIC BREATHING

One of the cornerstones of breath awareness and regulation in somatic therapy is diaphragmatic breathing, also known as belly breathing or abdominal breathing. This technique involves allowing the breath to originate from the depths of the abdomen rather than being confined to the upper chest.

To experience diaphragmatic breathing, find a comfortable position, either seated or lying down. Place one hand on your belly and one on your chest. As you inhale, allow your belly to expand outward, as if you are filling a balloon with air. You should feel your lower hand rise with the inhalation while your upper hand remains relatively still. As you exhale, allow your belly to contract gently inward, releasing the air fully. Continue this pattern, focusing on the sensations of expansion and release in your abdomen.

With practice, diaphragmatic breathing can become a powerful tool for self-regulation and healing. By engaging the diaphragm, we allow our lungs to fill more fully with air, increasing the amount of oxygen available to our body. This fuller, deeper breathing style helps to release chronic patterns of muscle tension and holding, particularly in the chest, shoulders, and belly. As we invite the breath to move freely through these regions, we may find layers of stored emotion and stress beginning to melt away.

In addition to its physical benefits, diaphragmatic breathing also has a profound impact on our nervous system. When we breathe deeply and fully into the belly, we stimulate the relaxation response of the parasympathetic nervous system. This branch of our autonomic nervous system is responsible for the "rest and digest" functions of the body, counterbalancing the "fight or flight" response of the sympathetic nervous system. By consciously shifting into diaphragmatic breathing, we send a signal of safety and calm to our body, helping to downregulate feelings of anxiety, overwhelm, or agitation.

EXERCISE: DIAPHRAGMATIC BREATHING

Diaphragmatic breathing, also known as belly breathing, is a fundamental somatic practice that involves breathing deeply into the lower belly. This technique engages the diaphragm, allowing for fuller, more efficient breaths. By establishing a rhythmic flow of deep belly breathing, you can promote relaxation, reduce stress, and enhance overall self-regulation. The goal of this practice is to cultivate a natural, full breathing pattern that originates in the belly and expands upward.

Guided Instructions

1. Find a comfortable position, either sitting upright or lying down. If seated, ensure your spine is straight but not rigid, and your shoulders are relaxed. If lying down, you may place a pillow under your knees for added comfort.

2. Place one hand on your belly, just below your navel. This will help you tune into the movement of your diaphragm as you breathe.

3. Begin by gently exhaling all the air out of your lungs. As you do so, feel your belly soften and contract inward.

4. Slowly inhale through your nose, focusing on expanding your belly outward first. Feel your hand rise as your diaphragm descends and your lower lungs fill with air.

5. Allow the inhalation to expand upward, filling your rib cage and upper chest. Avoid forcing or straining; allow the breath to flow smoothly and naturally.

6. Pause briefly at the top of the inhalation, then begin to exhale slowly through your mouth. Feel your belly gradually contract as your diaphragm rises, expelling the air from bottom to top.

7. Continue this breathing pattern, starting with belly expansion and filling upward on the inhale, then emptying from the top down on the exhale. Start with a slow, gentle pace and gradually deepen your breath as you find a comfortable rhythm.

8. If it helps, you can visualize a wave of breath moving up and down your torso or silently repeat a calming word or phrase to anchor your focus.

9. As you settle into the practice, notice the signs that you have achieved a proper diaphragmatic breathing rhythm: your belly rises and falls more noticeably than your chest, and you feel a sense of ease and spaciousness in your breath.

10. Continue for several minutes, allowing your breath to find its natural, unhurried pace. If your mind wanders, gently redirect your attention back to the sensation of breathing into your belly.

Closing

Take a few final deep breaths, savoring the sense of calm and groundedness that diaphragmatic breathing fosters. As you conclude the practice, carry this quality of easeful, full breathing with you into your daily life. Remember, you can return to this fundamental somatic practice anytime you wish to promote relaxation and self-regulation.

EXERCISE: REGULATING BREATH FOR CALM

Conscious breathing is a powerful tool for self-regulation, capable of shifting our physiological state from stressed to calm. By deliberately slowing and deepening the breath, we engage the parasympathetic nervous system, promoting relaxation throughout the mind and body. This practice offers a simple yet potent technique for harnessing the breath to induce a sense of tranquility and ease.

Guided Instructions

1. Begin by finding a comfortable posture, either seated or lying down. Ensure your spine is long but not rigid and your body feels supported and at ease.

2. Close your eyes and tune into your current breathing pattern. Notice the pace and depth of your breath without judgment or attempts to change it.

3. Now, gently deepen your breath, directing the inhalation low into your belly. Feel your abdomen expand as you fill your lungs from the bottom up.

4. Slowly exhale, allowing the breath to release from your body in a smooth, controlled manner. Extend the duration of your exhalation, aiming to make it slightly longer than your inhalation.

5. Establish a rhythmic breathing pattern where your exhale is longer than your inhale. You might silently count the breath, inhaling for a count of four and exhaling for a count of six.

6. If it feels comfortable, you can incorporate a brief pause at the end of each exhale, savoring the stillness before inhaling again.

7. Continue this pattern of deep, slow breathing, synchronizing your breath with a silent count, a calming word or phrase, or a soothing visual image.

8. As you maintain this conscious breathing rhythm, notice the signs that your body is shifting into a state of calm: your muscles soften, your mind grows quieter, and a sense of ease permeates your being.

9. If your mind wanders or your breath becomes shallow, gently redirect your attention back to the deep, slow rhythm of your inhalations and extended exhalations.

10. Remain with this calming breath for several minutes, allowing your mind and body to fully absorb the soothing effects of this practice.

Closing

As you complete the exercise, take a moment to appreciate the power of your breath to guide you into a state of calm and balance. Know that you can return to this simple practice anytime you need to down-regulate stress and promote a sense of inner peace. Carry the tranquility cultivated through this conscious breathing with you as you move forward in your day.

EXERCISE: PLAYFUL BREATHING EXERCISES

Conscious breathing practices do not always have to be somber. Engaging with the breath in playful, creative ways can inject a sense of lightness, joy, and spontaneity into your practice. These explorative exercises invite you to experience the breath in novel, unconventional forms, sparking a spirit of curiosity and wonder. By approaching the breath with a sense of play, we can discover new dimensions of this vital life force and deepen our relationship with it.

Guided Instructions

1. **Breath Sounds:** Begin by taking a few deep breaths, then start to exhale with voiced sounds. Experiment with different tones and qualities, like a soft "ha," a prolonged "sh," or a resonant "om." Notice how each sound vibrates uniquely in your body.

2. **Alternating Nostril Breathing:** Using your right thumb and ring finger, gently block off one nostril at a time as you breathe. Inhale through the left nostril, then close it and exhale through the right. Inhale through the right, then switch to exhale through the left. Continue this alternating pattern, observing the subtle shifts in your breath and mind.

3. **Breath Visualizations:** As you breathe, imagine the breath-taking on different visual forms. You might picture the inhalation as a stream of golden light filling your body or the exhalation as a gentle mist releasing tension. Let your creative imagination guide the process.

4. **Breath Movements:** Allow your breath to initiate organic, fluid movements in your body. You might sway side to side with each inhale and exhale or let your arms float up on the inhalation and drift down on the exhalation. Follow the natural impulses of your breath and move in ways that feel good.

5. **Mirrored Breathing:** Find a partner and sit facing each other. Begin to synchronize your breath, inhaling and exhaling together. You can even place your hands on each other's chest or belly to feel the shared rhythm. Notice how it feels to attune your breath with another.

6. **Animal Breaths:** Playfully emulate the breathing patterns of different creatures. Take short, quick breaths like a bunny or slow, deep breaths like a turtle. Imagine how a lion or a hummingbird might breathe and embody those qualities.

Closing

As you complete these playful breathing exercises, please take a moment to appreciate the fresh perspectives and insights they offer. Notice any shifts in your energy or mood and relish the sense of joyful aliveness the practices sparked. Remember that you can infuse your breath with this spirit of play and discovery anytime, letting it be a source of renewal and delight. Carry this sense of lighthearted presence with you as you move through your day.

EXERCISE: BREATH REGULATION AND PROGRESSIVE MUSCLE RELAXATION

Breath Regulation and Progressive Muscle Relaxation is an exercise that combines two effective relaxation techniques to promote deep relaxation, reduce stress and anxiety, and improve overall well-being. By focusing on slow, deep breathing while systematically tensing and relaxing different muscle groups, you can create a profound sense of physical and mental relaxation. This exercise is particularly helpful for those who experience chronic stress, muscle tension, sleep difficulties, or anxiety disorders.

Steps

1. Find a quiet, comfortable place where you can sit or lie down without disturbance. If sitting, choose a chair with good back support and ensure your feet are flat on the ground. If lying down, use a yoga mat or blanket for comfort, and support your head with a pillow if needed.

2. Close your eyes and take a few natural breaths, allowing your body to settle and your mind to become present. Notice any areas of tension or discomfort in your body without judgment.

3. Begin to focus on your breathing, consciously slowing and deepening each inhalation and exhalation. Inhale through your nose for a count of 4, allowing your belly to expand as your lungs fill with air. Hold your breath for a count of 2, then exhale slowly through your mouth for a count of 6, feeling your belly fall as you release the air.

4. Continue this slow, deep breathing pattern (inhale for 4, hold for 2, exhale for 6) throughout the exercise, maintaining a steady and comfortable rhythm.

5. As you breathe deeply, bring your attention to your feet and toes. On your next exhalation, gently tense the muscles in your feet and toes, scrunching them tightly. Hold this tension for 5-10 seconds, focusing on the sensation of tightness and contraction.

6. On your next inhalation, release the tension in your feet and toes, allowing them to relax completely. Notice the feeling of release and relief as you let go of the tension.

7. Move your attention up to your lower legs and calves. As you exhale, flex your feet and point your toes towards your face, engaging your calf muscles. Hold this tension for 5-10 seconds, synchronizing it with your deep breathing.

8. As you inhale, release the tension in your calves, allowing your feet to return to a neutral position. Feel the wave of relaxation spreading through your lower legs.

9. Continue this process of tensing and relaxing each muscle group in synchrony with your breath, moving progressively up through your body. Follow this sequence:

- Thighs and buttocks

- Hips and pelvis
- Stomach and lower back
- Chest and upper back
- Shoulders and neck
- Arms and hands
- Face (forehead, eyes, cheeks, mouth, and jaw)

10. For each muscle group, remember to tense on the exhalation, hold for 5-10 seconds, and then release and relax on the inhalation. Take your time and move slowly, allowing yourself to fully experience the sensations of tension and relaxation in each area.

11. After completing the sequence, continue your deep breathing for a few more cycles, scanning your body for any remaining areas of tension. If you notice any residual tightness, gently direct your breath to those areas and invite them to relax.

12. Finally, allow yourself to rest in this state of deep relaxation for a few minutes, savoring the sense of peace and tranquility you've cultivated. When you feel ready, gently wiggle your fingers and toes, take a few natural breaths, and slowly open your eyes.

Conclusion

Breath Regulation and Progressive Muscle Relaxation was included in this book because it offers a powerful combination of techniques to induce deep relaxation, reduce stress and anxiety, and promote overall well-being. By consciously slowing and deepening the breath while systematically tensing and relaxing different muscle groups, you can create a profound sense of physical and mental relaxation. Regular practice of this exercise can help to lower stress levels, improve sleep quality, and increase resilience in the face of life's challenges.

EXERCISE: COHERENT BREATHING AND HRV BIOFEEDBACK

Coherent Breathing and Heart Rate Variability Biofeedback is a powerful exercise that combines the practice of slow, rhythmic breathing with the use of biofeedback technology to help regulate the nervous system, reduce stress, and promote a state of physical and emotional coherence. Coherent breathing involves breathing at a rate of around 5-6 breaths per minute, which has been shown to optimize heart rate variability (HRV) and synchronize the body's various physiological systems. By using HRV biofeedback devices to monitor and guide your breathing, you can learn to achieve a state of coherence more easily and consistently, leading to improved health, emotional well-being, and overall resilience.

Steps

1. Begin by setting up your HRV biofeedback device according to the manufacturer's instructions. This may involve attaching sensors to your earlobes, fingertips, or chest and connecting the device to a computer or mobile app.

2. Find a quiet, comfortable place where you can sit or lie down without disturbance. If sitting, choose a chair with good back support and ensure your feet are flat on the ground. If lying down, use a yoga mat or blanket for comfort.

3. Place the HRV sensors on your body as directed and start the biofeedback software on your device. Most programs will display your heart rate, HRV, and coherence levels in real-time.

4. Close your eyes and take a few natural breaths, allowing your body to settle and your mind to become present. Notice any areas of tension or discomfort in your body without judgment.

5. Begin to focus on slowing and deepening your breath, aiming for a rate of around 5-6 breaths per minute. This typically involves inhaling for a count of 5-6 seconds and exhaling for the same count. Some biofeedback devices may provide visual or auditory cues to help guide your breathing pace.

6. As you continue to breathe slowly and deeply, bring your attention to the biofeedback display. Notice your heart rate variability pattern, which may initially appear chaotic or irregular.

7. With each breath, focus on creating a smooth, sinusoidal wave pattern in your HRV display. This indicates a state of coherence, where your heart rate is speeding up on the inhalation and slowing down on the exhalation in a rhythmic, balanced manner.

8. If your mind begins to wander or you find it difficult to maintain a slow breathing pace, gently redirect your attention back to your breath and the biofeedback display. Remember that developing coherence is a skill that improves with practice.

9. Continue the coherent breathing practice for 10-20 minutes or for as long as it feels comfortable for you. As you maintain this state of coherence, notice any sensations of calm, clarity, or emotional balance that arise.

10. When you're ready to conclude the practice, take a few natural breaths and gently open your eyes, taking a moment to reorient to your surroundings. Notice any shifts in your physical, emotional, or mental state.

11. Reflect on your experience and consider how you might integrate coherent breathing and HRV biofeedback into your daily routine, particularly during times of stress or challenge.

Conclusion

Coherent Breathing and Heart Rate Variability Biofeedback was included in this book because it offers a scientifically validated method for promoting physical, emotional, and mental well-being. By learning to breathe at a coherent rate and using biofeedback technology to guide and reinforce this practice, you can effectively regulate your nervous system, reduce stress and anxiety, and cultivate a greater sense of emotional balance and resilience. With regular practice, coherent breathing and HRV biofeedback can help you optimize your health, improve cognitive function, and enhance your overall quality of life.

EXERCISE: BREATH AWARENESS AND APPLIED RELAXATION

Breath Awareness and Applied Relaxation is an exercise that combines focused attention on the breath with the practical application of relaxation techniques in daily life. By developing a deep awareness of your breathing patterns and learning to use the breath as a tool for relaxation, you can cultivate a greater sense of calm, presence, and emotional balance. This exercise draws on principles from applied relaxation, a technique that involves learning to recognize early signs of stress or anxiety and applying relaxation skills in real-life situations. Through regular practice, Breath Awareness and Applied Relaxation can help you manage stress more effectively, improve sleep quality, and enhance overall well-being.

Steps

1. Find a quiet, comfortable place where you can sit or lie down without disturbance. If sitting, choose a chair with good back support and ensure your feet are flat on the ground. If lying down, use a yoga mat or blanket for comfort.

2. Close your eyes and take a few natural breaths, allowing your body to settle and your mind to become present. Notice any areas of tension or discomfort in your body without judgment.

3. Begin to focus your attention on your breath, observing the natural flow of inhalation and exhalation. Notice the sensation of the air moving through your nostrils or mouth, the rise and fall of your chest or belly, and any other physical sensations associated with breathing.

4. As you continue to observe your breath, notice any patterns or tendencies that arise. Do you tend to breathe shallowly or deeply? Quickly or slowly? Through your nose or mouth? Simply observe these patterns without trying to change them.

5. Now, begin to deepen and slow your breath, inhaling through your nose and exhaling through your mouth. Allow your belly to expand on the inhalation and fall on the exhalation, promoting a sense of relaxation and grounding.

6. As you maintain this deep, slow breathing pattern, begin to silently repeat a calming word or phrase in synchronization with your breath. For example, you might silently say "calm" on the inhalation and "ease" on the exhalation or "let" on the inhalation and "go" on the exhalation. Choose a word or phrase that resonates with you and promotes a sense of relaxation.

7. Continue this breath-focused relaxation for 5-10 minutes, allowing yourself to be fully present with the experience of breathing and the calming effects of your chosen word or phrase.

8. When you're ready to conclude the practice, take a few natural breaths and gently open your eyes, taking a moment to reorient to your surroundings.

9. Reflect on your experience and consider how you might apply this breath awareness and relaxation technique in daily life. Identify specific situations or triggers that tend to cause stress or anxiety, such as work deadlines, interpersonal conflicts, or daily commutes.

10. As you go about your day, practice noticing early signs of stress or tension in your body, such as a tightening of the jaw, shoulders, or stomach. When you notice these signs, take a moment to pause and apply the breath awareness and relaxation technique you practiced, using your chosen calming word or phrase to promote a sense of ease and groundedness.

11. With regular practice, Breath Awareness and Applied Relaxation can become a powerful tool for managing stress and promoting relaxation in daily life. Aim to integrate this technique into your daily routine, setting aside time for formal practice and applying it in real-life situations as needed.

Conclusion

Breath Awareness and Applied Relaxation was included in this book because it offers a practical and accessible way to cultivate relaxation skills and apply them in daily life. By developing a deep awareness of your breathing patterns and learning to use the breath as a tool for calming the mind and body, you can effectively manage stress, improve emotional regulation, and promote overall well-being. The integration of applied relaxation principles makes this exercise particularly valuable for navigating the challenges and stressors of daily life, empowering you to find greater ease, balance, and resilience in the face of difficulty.

PART III: ENGAGING WITH THE SOMA

7. MAPPING YOUR BODY'S WISDOM

As we deepen our journey into somatic healing and embodied self-discovery, we come to a profound realization: our bodies are not merely physical shells but living, sacred vessels that hold the entirety of our life experiences. Every joy and sorrow, every triumph and struggle, every belief and emotion leaves its imprint on our bodily landscape, shaping the way we move, feel, and express ourselves in the world.

In this chapter, we will explore the powerful practice of mapping your body's wisdom—a process of attuning to the deep intelligence and insight that resides within your embodied self. Through the lens of the somagram and body image exploration, you will learn to decode the messages and stories etched in your soma, cultivating a new level of self-understanding, compassion, and integration.

UNDERSTANDING THE SOMAGRAM

At the heart of this mapping process is a tool called the somagram—a kind of somatic autobiography that illuminates the ways in which your life experiences have been encoded in your body. Just as a written autobiography tells the story of your life through words and narrative, the somagram reveals the story of your embodiment through sensation, posture, movement, and breath.

The basic premise of the somagram is that our bodies are intricate tapestries woven from the threads of our lived experiences. Every significant event, relationship, and environment we encounter leaves its mark on our bodily being, shaping our patterns of physical and emotional response. These patterns can manifest as areas of chronic tension or pain, habits of postural collapse or rigidity, tendencies toward expansive or constricted breathing, and more.

By learning to read and decipher these somatic patterns, we gain profound insight into the deeper story of our lives—the narrative that lives beneath the surface of our conscious awareness. We begin to understand how our early experiences of safety or threat, our internalized beliefs about ourselves and the world, and our unresolved emotions and traumas continue to shape our embodied reality in the present moment.

This understanding is felt, visceral, and alive. As we attune to the somagram of our own body, we may find ourselves suddenly awash in vivid sense memories, long-forgotten scenes from our past that are stored in our cellular being. We may feel waves of grief, anger, or joy rising from the depths of our soma, seeking expression and release. We may discover areas of our body that feel numb, disconnected, or "off-limits," inviting us to bring the light of loving awareness to these exiled parts of ourselves.

Engaging with your somagram is a deeply personal and transformative process. It requires a willingness to venture into the uncharted territory of your own embodied experience and to meet whatever arises with curiosity, compassion, and care. While not always easy or comfortable, it is a profoundly rewarding journey of reclaiming your bodily sovereignty and integrating the disparate parts of your being.

EXPLORING BODY IMAGE WITH KINDNESS

One of the most powerful applications of the sonogram is in the realm of body image—the way we perceive, feel about and relate to our physical form. In today's society, there is an epidemic of body shame and disconnection fueled by narrow, oppressive ideals of beauty, health, and acceptability. From a young age, we are bombarded with messages that our bodies are not good enough as they are and that we must strive to conform to an impossible standard of perfection to be worthy of love and belonging.

These toxic narratives can become deeply internalized, shaping the way we inhabit and experience our somatic selves. We may develop patterns of harsh self-judgment, constantly monitoring and critiquing our body's appearance and performance. We may numb out or dissociate from the discomfort and vulnerability of embodied presence. We may engage in disordered eating, compulsive exercise, or other harmful behaviors in an attempt to control and manipulate our bodily being.

Somatic therapy invites us to reclaim our body as a sanctuary of a holistic being rather than an object of manipulation. This starts by addressing the toxic mainstream narratives around embodiment through critical analysis and self-reflection. With education and open dialogue, we can develop media literacy, recognize toxic messaging, and understand how oppressive beauty standards are used to disempower and generate profit.

From this foundation of awareness, we then engage our somagram to explore how these toxic narratives impact our embodied selfhood. With gentle curiosity, we map the specific ways body shame and discomfort live in our shape, posture, breath, and movement. We locate areas where we feel numb or exiled and areas of self-acceptance and appreciation. This detailed mapping brings unconscious patterns to light so we can develop targeted practices.

The key throughout is radical compassion—meeting our bodily being as it is, not as we think it "should" be. Through exercises like sensory self-appreciation, mirror work, and guided loving meditations on our form, we begin etching new grooves of care and respect. We focus on the miraculous functions and sensations our bodies provide rather than appearance. Slowly, we unlearn self-aggression and relearn body gratitude.

EXERCISE: CREATING YOUR BODY MAP

Body mapping is a powerful tool for enhancing embodiment and self-awareness. Through this exploratory process, you will cultivate a richer, more nuanced understanding of your unique bodily landscape. By engaging your creative, intuitive capacities, you will discover new ways of perceiving and relating to your somatic experience. Remember, there is no right or wrong way to body map— trust your inner wisdom and allow yourself to be surprised by what emerges.

Guided Instructions

1. Begin by finding a comfortable position, either seated or lying down. Have your drawing materials easily accessible.

2. Close your eyes and take a few deep, grounding breaths. Allow your awareness to settle into your body, noticing the general sensations that are present.

3. Slowly scan your attention through your body, starting at your feet and moving upward. Notice the different qualities of sensation in each area without judging or analyzing.

4. Now, choose one area of your body to focus on more deeply. It might be a place that feels particularly alive with sensation or an area that feels neutral or absent.

5. Spend a few minutes really tuning into the nuanced sensations in this area. Notice subtleties of temperature, texture, pressure, movement, or energy.

6. Allow an image to emerge that captures the felt sense of this body area. It might be a color, a shape, a symbol, or a metaphoric representation. Trust whatever arises, and do not censor yourself.

7. Open your eyes and intuitively draw the image that came to you. You can make an abstract full-body outline and depict the sensation within it or create a separate symbolic drawing. Let your creative expression flow freely.

8. Take your time with each body area, moving slowly and listening deeply. If you get stuck, return to your breath and the felt sensation, allowing a new image to surface.

9. Continue mapping your whole body in this way, staying open and curious about what each sensation must reveal. Remember, your body map is a living, evolving work of art.

10. When you feel complete, take a step back and observe your creation. Notice if any new insights or perspectives on your embodied experience emerge.

Closing

Take a moment to appreciate the rich tapestry of your somatic experience, as revealed through your body map. Honor the profound wisdom and creativity that resides within you and the courage it takes to engage in this intimate self-discovery. Remember that your body map is a sacred reflection of your inner world and a tool you can return to repeatedly to deepen your embodied awareness. As you conclude this practice, consider how you might integrate this new way of seeing and relating to your body into your daily life.

EXERCISE: BODY GRATITUDE PRACTICE

This practice is an invitation to cultivate a deep appreciation for the miraculous vessel that is your body. Through gentle inquiry into the wisdom and functionality of various bodily systems, we can foster a profound sense of gratitude and awe. By intentionally nurturing a positive somatic relationship in this way, we lay the foundation for greater overall well-being and self-compassion.

Guided Instructions

1. Begin by finding a comfortable posture, either seated or lying down. Take a few deep, grounding breaths to settle your awareness into your body.

2. Now, guide your attention to your skeletal structure. Reflect on the incredible strength and resilience of your bones and how they provide a sturdy framework for your body. Invite a sense of appreciation for this often-overlooked foundation.

3. Next, bring your focus to your cardiovascular system. Contemplate the ceaseless work of your heart, pumping life-giving blood to every cell. Marvel at the vast network of veins and arteries, delivering oxygen and nutrients with each beat. Allow gratitude to well up for this tireless circulation.

4. Shift your awareness to your digestive system. Consider the complex process of transforming food into fuel the intelligence of your body in extracting what it needs and eliminating what it does not. Offer appreciation for this nourishing capability.

5. Continue this inquiry with other bodily systems, such as your lungs and respiratory system, your nervous system, your sensory organs, your skin, and your reproductive organs. For each, please take a moment to reflect on its intricate functioning and the vital role it plays.

6. As you explore each area, invite a sense of awe and admiration. You might silently or verbally express gratitude with phrases like, "Thank you, lungs, for the gift of breath" or "I am so grateful for my eyes and the miracle of sight."

7. If your mind wanders, gently guide it back to the body area you were focusing on. Meet any physical discomfort or painful emotions with an extra dose of compassion and care.

8. When you have completed your gratitude scan, take a few deep breaths and feel the cumulative effect of this practice. Notice how your relationship with your body may have shifted, even if subtly.

Closing

As you finish this body gratitude practice, take a moment to bask in the profound appreciation you have cultivated. Consider making this a regular part of your self-care routine as a way to continually honor and nurture your relationship with your body. Remember, your body is a sacred vessel worthy of your deepest respect and care. Carry this sense of reverence and gratitude with you as you move through your day, letting it infuse your every interaction and experience.

EXERCISE: MINDFUL BODY MAPPING AND REFLECTION

The Mindful Body Mapping and Reflection exercise is a creative and reflective practice that combines mindfulness, body awareness, and self-reflection. This exercise invites you to create a visual representation of your bodily sensations, emotions, and experiences, fostering a deeper understanding of the mind-body connection. By engaging in this reflective process, you can gain valuable insights into your physical and emotional states, identify patterns or areas that need attention, and cultivate greater self-awareness and self-compassion.

Steps

1. Gather your materials: a piece of paper large enough to trace your body outline, colored pencils, markers, or crayons, and a comfortable space to lie down and draw.

2. Find a quiet, private area where you can lie down comfortably on the floor. Place the piece of paper beside you.

3. Take a few deep breaths, allowing your body to settle and your mind to become present. Close your eyes and bring your attention inward, noticing any physical sensations, emotions, or thoughts that arise.

4. When you feel ready, open your eyes and trace the outline of your body on the paper. You can either have someone else trace your outline or do it yourself by lying on the paper and tracing around your body with a pencil or marker.

5. Once you have your body outline, sit comfortably beside the paper and begin to focus on your bodily sensations. Start by bringing your attention to your feet and gradually scan upward through your body, noticing any areas of tension, relaxation, pain, or other sensations.

6. As you notice each sensation, choose a color that intuitively represents that feeling and color or mark the corresponding area on your body outline. For example, you might color an area of tension with red, an area of relaxation with blue, or an area of warmth with orange. Don't worry about creating a perfect representation; focus on the process of self-reflection and expression.

7. Continue this process of body scanning and coloring until you have filled in your entire body outline. Take your time, allowing yourself to be fully present with each sensation and emotion that arises.

8. Once you have completed your body map, take a step back and observe the image as a whole. Notice any patterns, insights, or surprises that emerge. Reflect on the following questions:

- What sensations or emotions are most prominent in your body map?
- Are there any areas that you left blank or had difficulty representing?
- What might your body be trying to communicate through these sensations and experiences?
- What areas of your body might need more attention, care, or healing?

9. Take some time to journal about your reflections, insights, and any intentions or actions you wish to take based on your body map. Consider how you might use this newfound awareness to support your physical, emotional, and overall well-being.

10. If desired, you can share your body map and reflections with a trusted friend, family member, or therapist for further discussion and support.

11. Close the practice by taking a few deep breaths and expressing gratitude for your body and the wisdom it holds. Keep your body map in a safe place for future reference and reflection.

Conclusion

The Mindful Body Mapping and Reflection exercise was included in this book because it offers a unique and creative way to explore the mind-body connection and cultivate self-awareness. By combining mindfulness, body scanning, and artistic expression, this practice allows you to access deeper insights into your physical and emotional experiences, identify areas for growth and healing, and develop greater self-compassion. Regular engagement in this reflective process can enhance your ability to listen to and understand your body's needs, ultimately promoting greater overall health and well-being.

EXERCISE: BREATH-FOCUSED BODY WISDOM MEDITATION

The Breath-Focused Body Wisdom Meditation is a powerful practice that combines mindful breathing with body awareness to help you access your inner wisdom and intuition. This exercise guides you through a process of turning inward, listening to your body's messages, and cultivating a deep sense of trust and connection with your physical and emotional experiences. By bringing your attention to your breath and body sensations, you can quiet the mind, reduce stress and anxiety, and tap into the innate wisdom and guidance that resides within you.

Steps

1. Find a quiet, comfortable space where you can sit or lie down without disturbance. If sitting, choose a chair or cushion that allows you to maintain a straight but relaxed spine. If lying down, use a yoga mat or blanket for comfort, and support your head with a pillow if needed.

2. Close your eyes and take a few deep breaths, allowing your body to settle and your mind to become present. Notice any areas of tension or discomfort in your body without judgment.

3. Begin to focus your attention on your breath, observing the natural flow of inhalation and exhalation. Notice the sensation of the air moving through your nostrils or mouth, the rise and fall of your chest or belly, and any other physical sensations associated with breathing.

4. As you continue to breathe mindfully, bring your attention to your feet. Imagine your breath flowing down to your feet with each inhalation and any tension or stress leaving your feet with each exhalation. Take a few breaths here, feeling your feet relax and ground into the earth.

5. Slowly move your attention up through your body, focusing on each area one at a time. As you bring your breath to each region, imagine it filling that part of your body with light, warmth, and relaxation. With each exhalation, release any tension, stress, or emotions that may be held in that area.

6. Move through your body in the following sequence, spending a few breaths on each area:

- Legs and knees
- Hips and pelvis
- Lower back and abdomen
- Upper back and chest
- Shoulders and neck
- Arms and hands
- Face and head

7. As you breathe into each area, be open to any sensations, emotions, or messages that may arise. Without judgment or analysis, acknowledge and accept whatever emerges, trusting that your body has the wisdom to share.

8. If you notice any areas of particular tension, pain, or emotion, spend a little extra time breathing into these regions. Imagine your breath as a soothing, healing energy, gently dissolving any discomfort or blockages.

9. Once you have completed the body scan, take a few deep breaths and imagine your entire body filled with light and vitality. Feel a sense of gratitude and appreciation for your body and its innate wisdom.

10. As you prepare to end the meditation, ask your body if it has any final messages or insights to share. Be open to any thoughts, feelings, or sensations that arise, trusting in the wisdom of your physical and emotional experiences.

11. Take a few deep breaths and gently open your eyes, bringing your awareness back to your surroundings. Take a moment to reflect on any insights or messages that arose during the practice, and consider how you might integrate this wisdom into your daily life.

Conclusion

The Breath-Focused Body Wisdom Meditation was included in this book because it offers a simple yet powerful way to access the deep well of wisdom and intuition that resides within the body. By combining mindful breathing with body awareness and self-inquiry, this practice helps to bridge the gap between the conscious mind and the body's innate intelligence. Regular practice of this meditation can help to reduce stress, improve emotional regulation, and cultivate a greater sense of trust and connection with oneself, ultimately leading to increased self-awareness, self-compassion, and overall well-being.

EXERCISE: HEART-CENTERED BODY WISDOM PRACTICE

The Heart-Centered Body Wisdom Practice is an exercise that combines the use of heart rate variability biofeedback (HRVB) with mindful body awareness to help you access your inner wisdom and cultivate a deeper sense of mind-body-heart connection. By focusing on your heart center and tuning into your body's sensations and messages while using HRVB technology, you can learn to balance your autonomic nervous system, reduce stress, and enhance your overall well-being. This practice is particularly useful for developing self-awareness, emotional regulation, and intuitive decision-making skills.

Steps

1. Begin by setting up your HRVB device according to the manufacturer's instructions. This may involve attaching a sensor to your earlobe, fingertip, or chest and connecting it to a smartphone app or computer software.

2. Find a quiet, comfortable space where you can sit without disturbance. Sit in a chair with your feet flat on the ground and your hands resting comfortably on your lap.

3. Close your eyes and take a few deep breaths, allowing your body to settle and your mind to become present. Notice any physical sensations, emotions, or thoughts that arise without judgment.

4. Place one hand on your heart center (in the middle of your chest) and focus your attention on this area. Take a moment to connect with the sensation of your hand on your chest and the subtle beating of your heart.

5. As you continue to breathe, imagine each inhalation flowing into your heart center, bringing a sense of warmth, light, and expansion. With each exhalation, imagine any stress, tension, or negative emotions releasing from your heart center, leaving you feeling more open, balanced, and at peace.

6. Now, shift your attention to the HRVB device and start the biofeedback session. Most devices will provide real-time feedback on your heart rate variability, often in the form of a graph or visual display.

7. As you observe your HRV data, continue to focus on your heart center and maintain a slow, deep breathing pattern. If your mind begins to wander, gently redirect your attention back to your heart

and breath.

8. While maintaining this heart-centered focus, bring to mind a question, issue, or decision that you would like to receive guidance on. It could be related to your health, relationships, career, or any other area of your life.

9. Silently ask your body and heart for wisdom and guidance on this matter. Trust that your body holds deep insight and knowledge that can help you navigate life's challenges and opportunities.

10. As you continue to breathe and focus on your heart center, be open to any sensations, emotions, images, or intuitive thoughts that arise. Notice if any areas of your body feel particularly activated or tingly, as this may indicate a message or insight trying to come through.

11. If any specific guidance or insights arise, take a moment to acknowledge and appreciate them. If no clear messages come through, trust that your body and heart are still communicating with you on a subtle level and that the answers will come in time.

12. When you feel ready, take a few deep breaths and gently open your eyes, bringing your awareness back to your surroundings. Take a moment to reflect on any insights or sensations that arose during the practice.

13. Close the HRVB session and remove the sensor, taking a moment to appreciate your body and heart for their wisdom and support.

Conclusion

The Heart-Centered Body Wisdom Practice was included in this book because it offers a unique and powerful way to access the deep well of wisdom and intuition that resides within the body and heart. By combining HRVB technology with mindful body awareness and self-inquiry, this exercise helps to cultivate a stronger connection between the mind, body, and heart, enabling you to tap into your inner guidance system and make more aligned and authentic choices. Regular practice of this technique can help to reduce stress, improve emotional regulation, and enhance overall well-being by fostering a deeper sense of self-trust and self-attunement.

8. THE JOY OF MOVEMENT

As embodied beings, we are born to move. From the first miracle of our infant muscles learning to grasp and crawl to the wild abandon of childhood play to the intricate choreographies of our adult lives - movement is the native language of our soma. It is through movement that we express our deepest emotions, explore our physical capabilities, and connect with the world around us.

Yet, many of us have become disconnected from this vital, life-giving capacity amidst our modern sedentary lifestyles. We spend hours sitting still, barely noticing our body's impulse to stretch and sway. We often view exercise as a chore rather than a celebration of our embodied aliveness.

Somatic therapy seeks to reawaken and reclaim the transformative power of movement, recognizing its intimate connection to our mental, emotional, and spiritual well-being. By bringing conscious awareness to our movement practices, we tap into a wellspring of healing, vitality, and joy.

THE ROLE OF MOVEMENT IN SOMATIC THERAPY

Movement is a powerful vehicle for expression, release, and integration in somatic healing work. Mindful, intentional movement creates space for the body to tell its stories, reveal hidden holdings and habits, and discover new possibilities of ease and fluidity.

Think of a time when you were feeling stressed or overwhelmed. Your body likely reflected this inner state through patterns of tension and constriction. The simple act of standing up, shaking out your limbs, and taking a few deep breaths can be a profound act of self-care and regulation.

As we move with mindfulness, we unwind patterns of tension, release pent-up energy and emotion, and allow the body to find its natural rhythm and flow. This differs from the unconscious, habitual movements we often engage in throughout our day, which tend to reinforce existing patterns of limitation.

When we bring presence and curiosity to our movement, we open up possibilities for somatic discovery and transformation. We become more attuned to the subtle sensations and impulses arising from within, cultivating a deeper sense of interoceptive awareness - the ability to feel and interpret our internal landscape.

SUGGESTIONS FOR EMBODIED MOVEMENT PRACTICES

There are countless ways to bring the principles of somatic therapy into your movement routines. The key is to approach movement with curiosity, playfulness, and self-compassion.

Mindful walking is an accessible and profound practice. Bring your full attention to the felt sense of your feet contacting the earth, the swing of your hips and spine, and the flow of your breath. Notice areas of tension and invite ease into your gait. Experiment with different paces and qualities of energy.

Authentic movement, a form of self-directed, improvised motion, allows the body to express itself freely and spontaneously. Create a safe, non-judgmental space to listen and respond to your body's impulses and witness the stories and emotions expressed through movement.

Yoga is another rich tradition of embodied movement that can be a powerful ally in somatic healing work. Its emphasis on mindful alignment, coordinating movement with breath, and cultivating inner stillness sets it apart. Practiced with care, yoga can help release chronic tension and connect with our innate capacity for joy.

Dance can be one of the most liberating and transformative embodied movement practices. Surrendering to the pulse of music and letting the body express itself in uninhibited ways can evoke a sense of freedom and vitality, tapping into a deep wellspring of creativity and life force.

The specific practices that resonate with you will be unique to your own body and preferences. The key is to cultivate a loving, playful, and nourishing relationship with your moving body.

EXERCISE: EXPLORING MICRO-MOVEMENTS

This practice is designed to enhance your interoceptive awareness of the subtle, often unnoticed movements within your body. By tuning into these micro-movements, you will discover a new layer of embodied experience—the living, pulsating nature of your soma. Bringing curiosity and focused attention to this subtle realm can deepen your sense of vitality and presence. Approach this practice with a spirit of open, non-judgmental exploration.

Guided Instructions

1. Begin by finding a comfortable position, either seated or lying down. Take a few deep, grounding breaths to settle your awareness into your body.

2. First, bring your attention to your bodily sensations as a whole. Notice the general aliveness and vibration that permeates your entire being.

3. Now, choose a specific area of your body to zoom in on, such as your hands, feet, or abdomen. Let your attention gently land here.

4. Adopt an open, quasi-meditative awareness, observing the sensations in this area without analyzing or judging. Be present with what is.

5. Notice any subtle pulsations, shifting, or fluid movements within this body part. You might feel the delicate pulse of blood pumping, the slight expansion and contraction with each breath, or the ephemeral tingling of energy.

6. Allow yourself to be captivated by these micro-movements, observing them with a childlike sense of wonder. Notice their rhythm, texture, and aliveness.

7. When you feel ready, slowly shift your micro-attention to another area of your body. Again, tune into the nuanced dance of sensations happening just beneath the surface.

8. Continue this process of focused exploration, gently moving your awareness through different body regions. Maintain a sense of lightness and curiosity, letting yourself be surprised by what you discover.

9. If your mind wanders, acknowledge the thoughts and gently guide your attention back to the micro-sensations you were observing.

10. As you conclude the practice, take a moment to feel the effect of this subtle attunement. Notice any shifts in your sense of embodiment or overall presence.

Closing

Take a moment to appreciate the profound wisdom and aliveness you have received through this practice. By attuning to the subtle dimension of micro-movements, you affirm the intrinsic vitality of your embodied experience. Consider integrating this type of focused exploration into your daily life—perhaps while waiting in line, sitting in a meeting, or lying in bed at night. Each moment offers an opportunity to deepen your embodied presence. Carry this sense of intimate, curious attention with you as you re-engage with your day.

EXERCISE: EXPRESSIVE MOVEMENT PLAY

This practice invites you to explore spontaneous, intuitive self-expression through movement. By engaging in this somatic play, you will break free from habitual patterns and discover new possibilities for embodied creativity. There is no right or wrong way to approach this practice—allow yourself to be guided by your inner impulses and the wisdom of your body. Embrace a spirit of open, non-judgmental experimentation as you embark on this movement journey.

Guided Instructions

1. Begin by finding an open space where you have room to move freely. If it feels comfortable, you may choose to remove your socks and shoes to ground your bare feet on the earth.

2. Take a few deep breaths, releasing any self-consciousness or expectations. Remind yourself that this is a space for authentic, unfiltered expression.

3. Guide your awareness through a brief body scan, noticing any sensations, emotions, or energy that are present. Allow your posture to reflect this inner experience, perhaps crouching low, reaching high, or hugging yourself.

4. From this place of embodied awareness, begin to invite organic, spontaneous movements to emerge. Let your body lead the way, following its natural impulses and curiosities.

5. Explore various levels, moving low to the ground, then reaching high into the space above you. Experiment with various shapes, from sharp angles to soft curves. Play with rhythm, alternating between quick, staccato movements and slow, fluid ones.

6. Remember, there is no need to make your movements beautiful, graceful, or performative. This is a space for raw, honest expression. Allow yourself to be wild, silly, or awkward—whatever authentically arises.

7. Permit yourself to let sounds and vocalizations emerge alongside your movements. Grunt, sigh, laugh, or cry out—let your body express the full spectrum of your experience.

8. If strong emotions arise, allow them to move through you. Dance your anger, shake out your sorrow, or sway with your joy. Trust that your body can metabolize and integrate these feelings.

9. Periodically, take a pause and return to stillness. Notice how your body feels in the aftermath of the movement. Then, let the next organic impulse arise, repeating the cycle of expression and repose.

10. As you near the end of your practice, take a few minutes to rest in a posture that feels grounding and stabilizing. Feel the effects of this somatic play in your body, heart, and mind.

Closing
Take a moment to appreciate yourself for engaging in this courageous act of self-expression. Honor the wisdom of your body and the authenticity of your experience exactly as it is. Consider making this type of expressive movement play a regular part of your embodiment practice as a way to continually deepen your relationship with your somatic creativity. As you move through the rest of your day, notice how this experience of uninhibited expression may have shifted your perspective or opened new possibilities. Carry this sense of embodied freedom and aliveness with you, letting it infuse all that you do.

EXERCISE: AUTHENTIC MOVEMENT EXPLORATION

Authentic Movement is a therapeutic modality that facilitates somatic unfolding and embodied self-discovery. In this practice, you will remove habitual controls and allow your innate movement impulses to emerge spontaneously. The intention is to enhance your embodied self-awareness and attunement to your body's wisdom. Approach this exploration with a sense of open curiosity, letting go of any expectations or judgments.

Guided Instructions
1. Begin by finding a private, enclosed space where you can move freely without obstructions. This might be a room in your home, a studio, or an outdoor area. Ensure that you have enough space to

explore a range of movements.

2. To create a transitional boundary and mark the start of your practice, walk the perimeter of your space. This ritual can help you shift into a more embodied state of awareness.

3. If it feels comfortable, remove your socks and shoes, as well as any extra layers of clothing. This can enhance your sensory experience and connection to your body.

4. Guide your awareness inward through a brief body scan meditation. Notice any sensations, emotions, or energy that are present. Allow yourself to settle into a grounded, centered state.

5. From this place of embodied presence, invite spontaneous micro-movements to emerge. This might begin with subtle shifts in your breath, small sways, or gentle rhythms in your body.

6. As you continue, allow these micro-movements to iterate and expand organically. Follow the natural evolution of your body's impulses, letting the movements grow, speed or complexity.

7. Explore a range of expressive shapes, gestures, and qualities. You might find yourself reaching, twisting, spiraling, or undulating. Let your body lead the way, surrendering to its innate wisdom.

8. Periodically, return to stillness and notice the aftereffects of the movement. Then, when you feel ready, reinitiate the process, allowing a new cycle of authentic movement to unfold.

9. Remember, there is no need to make your movements beautiful, graceful, or cohesive. The goal is not to create an aesthetic dance but to feel and follow your body's genuine impulses.

10. At times, you may find it helpful to close your eyes to deepen your internal experience. This can facilitate greater attunement to your somatic sensations and impulses.

11. Continue this process of embodied exploration for as long as desired, honoring your body's natural ebbs and flows. When you feel complete, take a few moments to rest in stillness, integrating the experience.

Closing

As you conclude this Authentic Movement exploration, take a moment to appreciate your body's innate wisdom and creativity. Notice any shifts in your embodied self-awareness or sense of attunement. Consider integrating this practice into your regular self-care routine as a way to continually deepen your relationship with your somatic experience. Trust that the insights and discoveries that emerged through this process will continue to unfold and support your journey of embodied healing and growth.

EXERCISE: HEART-CENTERED MOVEMENT EXPLORATION

Heart-Centered Movement Exploration is an exercise that combines the use of heart rate variability biofeedback (HRVB) with mindful, expressive movement to help you cultivate a deeper sense of mind-body-heart connection, emotional regulation, and self-awareness. By focusing on your heart center and allowing your movements to be guided by your breath and emotional state, you can tap into a powerful source of inner wisdom, creativity, and resilience. This practice is particularly useful for developing greater self-compassion, authenticity, and the ability to navigate life's challenges with grace and ease.

Steps

1. Begin by setting up your HRVB device according to the manufacturer's instructions. This may involve attaching a sensor to your earlobe, fingertip, or chest and connecting it to a smartphone app or computer software.

2. Find a quiet, comfortable space where you can move freely without disturbance. Ensure you have enough room to extend your arms and legs in all directions.

3. Stand with your feet hip-width apart or seated if preferred. Take a moment to feel your connection to the ground beneath you, noticing the sensation of your feet on the floor or your body supported by a chair.

4. Close your eyes or maintain a soft, unfocused gaze. Take a few deep breaths, allowing your body to settle and your mind to arrive in the present moment.

5. Place one hand on your heart center (in the middle of your chest) and focus your attention on this area. Notice the sensation of your hand on your chest and the subtle beating of your heart.

6. As you continue to breathe, imagine each inhalation flowing into your heart center, bringing a sense of warmth, light, and expansion. With each exhalation, imagine any stress, tension, or negative emotions releasing from your heart center, leaving you feeling more open, balanced, and at peace.

7. Now, shift your attention to the HRVB device and start the biofeedback session. Most devices will provide real-time feedback on your heart rate variability, often in the form of a graph or visual display.

8. As you observe your HRV data, continue to focus on your heart center and maintain a slow, deep breathing pattern. Notice any changes in your emotional state or physical sensations as you continue to breathe and focus on your heart.

9. Begin to allow your body to move in response to your breath and the sensations in your heart center. This may start with small, subtle movements, such as gently swaying side to side or circling your arms in front of your chest. Allow your movements to be organic and unplanned, following the natural impulses of your body and heart.

10. As you feel more comfortable, start to explore larger, more expressive movements. You might reach your arms overhead on an inhalation or bend forward and release your upper body on an exhalation. Allow your heart and breath to guide your movements, letting each gesture flow seamlessly into the next.

11. Experiment with different qualities and textures of movement, noticing how they affect your HRV and emotional state. You might try soft, flowing movements to cultivate a sense of ease and compassion or strong, powerful movements to tap into feelings of courage and resilience.

12. Throughout the practice, maintain an open and curious attitude without judgment or expectation. If your mind starts to wander or criticize, gently redirect your attention back to your heart center and the sensations of your moving body.

13. Continue to move and explore for 10-15 minutes or for as long as it feels comfortable and meaningful for you. Allow yourself to be surprised and moved by the wisdom and intelligence of your own heart and body.

14. As you prepare to end the practice, gradually slow down your movements and deepen your breath. Take a few moments to stand or sit in stillness, feeling the energy and aliveness in your heart center and throughout your entire body.

15. Gently open your eyes, if they were closed, and take a moment to reorient to your surroundings. Notice any shifts in your mood, energy level, or overall sense of well-being.

16. Close the HRVB session and remove the sensor, taking a moment to appreciate and thank your body and heart for their guidance and support.

17. Take a moment to reflect on your experience. What did you learn about yourself and your emotional landscape through this practice? How might you integrate this heart-centered awareness into your daily life and relationships?

Conclusion

Heart-Centered Movement Exploration was included in this book because it offers a transformative way to connect with your deepest self and cultivate greater emotional intelligence, resilience, and self-compassion. By combining the power of HRVB technology with mindful, expressive movement and a focus on the heart center, this practice helps you to access and embody the wisdom of your own emotions, intuition, and inner guidance. Regular engagement with this exercise can lead to greater self-awareness, authenticity, and the ability to navigate life's ups and downs with grace, courage, and compassion. Ultimately, Heart-Centered Movement Exploration is an invitation to trust in the power of your own heart and to live from a place of deep connection, purpose, and joy.

EXERCISE: AUTHENTIC MOVEMENT WITH PROGRESSIVE MUSCLE RELAXATION

Authentic Movement with Progressive Muscle Relaxation is an exercise that combines the somatic practice of authentic movement with the relaxation technique of progressive muscle relaxation (PMR). Authentic movement involves allowing the body to move spontaneously and expressively without judgment or expectation. By incorporating PMR, which involves systematically tensing and relaxing different muscle groups, you can release physical tension and cultivate a deeper sense of embodiment and self-awareness. This practice can be particularly helpful for those who struggle with self-judgment or inhibition, as it encourages a kind and accepting attitude towards the body and its natural impulses.

Steps

1. Find a quiet, private space where you can move freely without interruption. Ensure you have enough room to move in all directions and that the floor is comfortable and safe for movement.

2. Begin by standing or lying down in a comfortable position. Take a few deep breaths, allowing your body to settle and your mind to become present.

3. Starting with your feet and toes, gently tense the muscles in this area, holding the tension for 5-7 seconds. As you tense, notice the sensation of tightness and contraction in your feet and toes.

4. On an exhalation, release the tension, allowing your feet and toes to relax completely. Notice the sensation of release and letting go as your feet and toes soften and become heavy.

5. Move your attention up to your lower legs and calves. Again, tense the muscles in this area for 5-7 seconds, noticing the sensation of tension and contraction.

6. On an exhalation, release the tension, allowing your calves and lower legs to relax completely. Notice the sense of release and letting go as your legs become soft and heavy.

7. Continue this process of tensing and relaxing each muscle group, moving up through your body in the following sequence: thighs, hips and buttocks, stomach, chest, back, shoulders, arms and hands, neck, and face.

8. Once you have completed the PMR sequence, take a few moments to scan your body, noticing any areas that feel particularly relaxed or at ease. Allow yourself to rest in this state of physical relaxation for a few breaths

9. When you feel ready, begin to allow your body to move spontaneously and expressively without planning or controlling your movements. This may involve small, subtle gestures or larger, more expansive movements. Allow your body to lead the way, following its natural impulses and curiosities.

10. As you continue to move, try to let go of any judgment, self-criticism, or expectation. If you notice

your mind starting to judge or control your movements, gently redirect your attention back to the sensation of your body moving in space.

11. Explore different qualities and textures of movement, such as fast or slow, strong or gentle, fluid or staccato. Allow yourself to be surprised and delighted by the unique ways your body wants to move and express itself.

12. If emotions or memories arise during the movement, allow them to be expressed through your body safely and authentically. Trust that your body has its wisdom and intelligence and that it knows how to move in a way that supports your healing and growth.

13. Continue the authentic movement exploration for 10-20 minutes or for as long as it feels comfortable and meaningful for you. When you feel ready to end the practice, gradually slow down your movements, coming to a place of stillness and rest.

14. Take a few deep breaths, feeling the aliveness and presence in your body. Notice any shifts in your emotional state or sense of embodiment.

15. Gently open your eyes, if they were closed, and take a moment to reorient to your surroundings. Thank your body for its wisdom and expression and for the opportunity to connect with your authentic self through movement.

Conclusion

Authentic Movement with Progressive Muscle Relaxation was included in this book because it offers a powerful way to cultivate embodiment, self-awareness, and emotional authenticity. By combining the freedom and spontaneity of authentic movement with the release and relaxation of PMR, this practice helps to create a safe and supportive container for self-discovery and self-expression. Regular engagement with this exercise can lead to greater self-acceptance, creativity, and the ability to navigate life's challenges with grace and resilience. Ultimately, Authentic Movement with PMR is an invitation to trust in the wisdom of your own body and to embrace the fullness and richness of your authentic self.

9. ALIGNING WITH YOUR AUTHENTIC SELF

In the journey of embodied healing and growth, one of the most profound shifts we can make is moving from somatic misalignment to deep, authentic alignment with our true self. This alignment is a holistic reorientation of our being—a coming home to the innate wisdom, beauty, and integrity that resides within us.

At the heart of this process is an exploration of the intimate relationship between our posture and the emotional world. The way we hold and organize our physical structure directly reflects our inner landscape, a somatic expression of our beliefs, habits, and histories.

THE CONNECTION BETWEEN POSTURE AND EMOTION

Consider a time when you felt anxious, fearful, or insecure. Your body likely responded by contracting and collapsing inward, reinforcing the emotional narrative of vulnerability and threat. In contrast, when feeling confident, open, and at ease, your body may have been upright, relaxed, and expansive, embodying the emotional qualities of safety, connection, and trust.

These examples illustrate a fundamental principle of somatic psychology: our posture both reflects and reinforces our emotional reality. Inhabiting a posture of constriction limits our capacity for breath, movement, and vitality, signaling to our nervous system that we are under threat. Conversely, aligning in a posture of openness creates the physiological conditions for greater ease, flow, and aliveness, communicating safety and support.

The first step in aligning with our authentic self is bringing mindful awareness to our habitual postural patterns. These patterns, often developed in response to stress, trauma, or self-protection, can become so ingrained that we no longer notice them. By identifying and exploring these patterns with curiosity and compassion, we begin to unwind the layers of tension and holding that keep us stuck in somatic inauthenticity.

REALIGNING WITH YOUR EMBODIED TRUTH

The journey of postural alignment is about releasing tension and constriction that disconnect us from our embodied truth. It is about listening deeply to our soma's wisdom and allowing our natural, organic alignment to emerge from within.

This realignment process involves gradually unwinding physical patterns accumulated over a lifetime. Gentle, mindful movement practices like yoga or Feldenkrais can help release chronic holding, restore fluidity, and ease our structure. Somatic awareness practices, such as body scans or breathwork, deepen our felt sense of presence and connection.

As we release physical armoring, we create space for a more authentic and aligned expression of our being to arise, discovering freedom and vitality in our posture. This process is integral to our emotional and spiritual growth—as we learn to stand tall in our authentic alignment, we also stand tall in our values, boundaries, and deepest truths.

The journey of alignment is ongoing, with inevitable challenges and setbacks. Meeting these moments with patience and self-compassion is key, remembering that healing is a spiral path of return.

As we continue realigning with our embodied truth, we may notice subtle shifts in how we move through the world—standing taller, speaking more authentically, acting with greater purpose and integrity. We may discover ease and flow in our relationships, connecting more deeply and honestly with others.

The gift of postural alignment is coming home to ourselves, reclaiming our birthright as embodied beings of love, wisdom, and truth. When we take our stand in the sacred alignment of our being, we become a force of healing and transformation in the world.

EXERCISE: EMBODYING STRENGTH AND CONFIDENCE

This practice invites you to explore the somatic experience of strength and confidence. By consciously embodying these qualities through posture, movement, and intention, you can begin to install new mind-body patterns of empowerment. Regularly accessing these embodied states can help you cultivate a deeper sense of inner strength and self-assurance. Approach this practice with a spirit of curiosity and self-compassion, knowing that you are planting seeds for positive growth and change.

Guided Instructions

1. Begin by finding an open stance and planting your feet firmly onto the ground. Feel your connection to the earth beneath you, allowing it to support and stabilize you.

2. Take a few deep, grounding breaths into your belly. With each inhalation, feel your body expanding and filling with vitality. With each exhalation, release any tension or self-doubt.

3. Gradually guide your posture into an upright position, stacking your spine and opening your chest. Roll your shoulders back and down, creating a sense of spaciousness across your heart center.

4. Bring a gentle lift to your chin, allowing your gaze to be steady and forward-facing. Soften your jaw and brow, inviting a sense of ease and openness in your facial expression.

5. As you hold this posture of confidence, begin to internally affirm your strength and capability. You might silently say to yourself, "I am strong," "I am capable," or "I trust in my resilience."

6. Experiment with different powerful shapes and stances. You might place your hands on your hips, take a wide warrior stance, or reach your arms overhead in a victorious "V" shape. Allow yourself to

play with embodying confidence in your unique way.

7. Notice how these postures and movements feel in your body. What sensations arise as you inhabit this empowered state? Where do you feel your strength and confidence most vividly?

8. Give yourself permission to fully embrace and savor this somatic experience. If any self-consciousness or doubt arises, gently acknowledge it and then re-focus on your embodied sensations of power and self-assurance.

9. As you continue the practice, let your experience organically shift and change. You might find yourself drawn to more dynamic, expansive movements or settling into a quiet, centered stillness. Trust your body's wisdom and follow its lead.

10. When you feel ready to close the practice, take a few deep breaths and gently release any held postures or shapes. Take a moment to sense the aftereffects of this embodiment in your physical, emotional, and mental state.

Closing

Take a moment to appreciate yourself for engaging in this practice of embodied empowerment. Acknowledge the courage and openness it takes to explore new somatic possibilities. Consider integrating this type of embodiment practice into your daily life, perhaps as a morning ritual or to prepare for challenging situations. Trust that each time you consciously inhabit strength and confidence in your body, you are reinforcing these qualities in your mind and spirit. Carry this sense of empowered presence with you as you move forward in your day, knowing that you can meet whatever arises with grounded self-assurance.

EXERCISE: POSTURE CHECK-IN

This practice is designed to enhance your somatic awareness of postural habits and patterns. By bringing conscious attention to your alignment and muscle tension, you can begin to release unconscious gripping and holding in the body. Improving your posture in this way can lead to increased vitality, ease, and embodied presence. Approach this practice with a spirit of gentle inquiry and self-care, knowing that even small shifts can make a significant difference in your overall well-being.

Guided Instructions

1. Begin by settling into a comfortable seated or standing position. Take a few deep breaths, grounding your awareness into your body.

2. Guide your attention through a brief body scan, starting at the crown of your head and moving downward. Notice any areas of tightness, constriction, or discomfort.

3. As you scan, pay particular attention to common tension areas such as the jaw, neck, shoulders, and

lower back. If you notice any gripping or holding, consciously soften and release these areas on an exhalation.

4. Bring your awareness to your spine, sensing its natural, unstrained alignment. Imagine a string gently lifting the crown of your head towards the sky, lengthening your spine without creating rigidity.

5. Make any small adjustments needed to optimize your alignment, such as tucking your chin slightly, rolling your shoulders back and down, or engaging your core muscles. Avoid forcing or pushing your body into position; instead, invite a sense of released uprightness.

6. Bring your attention to your foundation, whether that is your feet on the floor or your sit bones on the chair. Notice the quality of your connection to this base of support. If needed, make small adjustments to feel more grounded and stable.

7. Explore some gentle movements that encourage a sense of length and spaciousness in your spine. You might try a few seated cat-cow tilts, some shoulder rolls, or a standing side bend. Let these movements be fluid and organic rather than forced or strained.

8. Throughout the practice, keep inviting your body back to a state of release, aligned uprightness. Notice how even small postural shifts can impact your breathing, energy levels, and overall sense of well-being.

9. As you move through your day, set an intention to periodically check in with your posture. You might use natural transitions, like standing up from your desk or waiting in line, as opportunities to re-establish healthy alignment.

10. Remember, improving posture is a gradual process of bringing awareness, releasing holding patterns, and reinforcing new habits. Be patient and compassionate with yourself as you engage in this ongoing practice.

Closing

Please take a moment to appreciate your body for its incredible capacity to adapt and realign. Notice any positive shifts, however small, in your posture, breathing, or overall sense of ease. Consider integrating this type of postural check-in into your daily routine, whether that is setting a reminder on your phone or linking it to an existing habit. Trust that each time you bring loving awareness to your alignment, you are supporting your body's innate healing potential. Carry this sense of embodied uprightness with you as you move through your day, knowing that you have the power to optimize your posture and well-being.

EXERCISE: ALIGNING WITH YOUR CORE

This practice is designed to enhance your awareness and engagement of your body's core muscles. By learning to access and activate your core, you can develop a more integrated sense of grounding, stability, and alignment. Regularly practicing core connection can lead to improved posture, breath support, and overall embodied presence. Approach this exercise with a spirit of gentle curiosity, exploring the subtle sensations and adjustments that arise as you attune to your body's center.

Guided Instructions

1. Begin by finding an upright seated or standing position. Take a few deep breaths, bringing your awareness into your torso area.

2. Place your hands on your lower abdomen, just below your navel. As you inhale, feel your belly expand into your hands. As you exhale, notice how your abdominal muscles naturally draw inward.

3. On your next exhalation, gently engage your deep abdominal muscles as if you are hollowing out your lower belly. Imagine drawing your navel back towards your spine.

4. Maintain this gentle core engagement as you continue to breathe, keeping your spine erect but not rigid. Notice how this activation provides a sense of support and lift through your torso.

5. Experiment with subtle movements from this centered, engaged core. You might try a gentle twist to the right and left, keeping your hips stable and initiating the rotation from your abdomen.

6. As you move, pay attention to the interplay between your core and your breath. Notice how drawing your low belly in on the exhale can intensify core engagement.

7. Return to a neutral position, maintaining the sense of length in your spine and the gentle drawing-in of your lower abdomen. Feel your sit bones grounding down as your crown lifts, creating a sense of integrated alignment.

8. Continue to explore small movements and adjustments, always returning to this place of centered core engagement. You might try a subtle pelvic tilt or a side-to-side sway, noticing how your core supports and stabilizes you.

9. Throughout the practice, keep attuning to the sensations in your core. If you notice yourself gripping or holding, gently release and re-engage with a sense of ease and vitality.

10. As you complete the practice, take a moment to sense the aftereffects of this core alignment. Notice any shifts in your posture, breath, or overall sense of embodied stability.

Closing

Please take a moment to appreciate your body's innate wisdom and its capacity for integrated alignment. Notice any positive shifts, however subtle, in your posture, breathing, or overall sense of centered grounding.

10. EMBODYING YOUR BOUNDARIES

In the journey of embodied healing and growth, developing the ability to set and maintain healthy boundaries is crucial. Boundaries are the invisible but powerful lines we draw around ourselves to define what is and is not okay, what we will and will not allow into our space, energy, and experience. They are the guardians of our sovereignty and the protectors of our sacred selfhood.

However, for many, boundaries can feel abstract or intimidating, especially if we grew up in families or cultures where boundaries were nonexistent or constantly violated. In somatic therapy, we recognize that boundaries are deeply embodied realities rooted in our capacity for self-attunement—the ability to tune in to our own needs, desires, and limits and to honor them as sacred and non-negotiable.

UNDERSTANDING THE IMPORTANCE OF BOUNDARIES

Boundaries are a function of self-love and self-respect, communicating that our needs and desires are valid and worthy of consideration. With healthy boundaries, we can say yes to what nourishes us and no to what drains us, navigating relationships and interactions with clarity, integrity, and authenticity.

Poor or porous boundaries often lead to enmeshment, codependency, or violation, leaving us feeling like we are constantly giving more than we are receiving or that our sense of self is being eroded. The consequences can be profound, affecting us physically (chronic tension, fatigue, illness), emotionally (anxiety, resentment, depletion), and spiritually (disconnection from our truth, purpose, and power).

DEVELOPING EMBODIED BOUNDARY SETTING

Boundary setting is a skill that can be learned and cultivated through somatic therapy practices. One key way to embody boundaries is through breath. When feeling overwhelmed or drained by an interaction, we can use our breath to create space, assert our autonomy, and regulate our nervous system. Taking a deep, intentional breath can help us ground ourselves in our center, reminding us of our sovereignty and strength.

Posture and physical presence also communicate volumes about our sense of self-worth, agency, and autonomy. Standing tall with feet planted firmly, spine upright, and chest open conveys a message of self-possession and self-respect. We can practice embodying this boundary-setting presence in daily interactions, realigning with our center and truth.

Voice and tonality are potent tools for embodying boundaries. Speaking with a firm, grounded tone from our belly can convey authority, clarity, and conviction. Trusting our voice as an instrument of our truth allows us to advocate for our needs and desires.

Embodied boundary setting may not always be comfortable, especially for those with histories of trauma or marginalization. We may encounter fear, guilt, self-doubt, resistance, or pushback when asserting ourselves. This is where compassionate self-boundaries come in—treating ourselves with the same kindness, respect, and consideration we would extend to a beloved friend or child, honoring our limits, and prioritizing our needs.

Self-boundaries form the foundation of all other boundary work. When we develop a deep sense of our worth, we naturally attract and create relationships and experiences that reflect this inner alignment. Boundaries become less about defense and more about joyful, authentic expression.

Embodying boundaries is a journey of reclaiming our sacred selfhood, standing in the truth of who we are and what we deserve. It is a journey of courage, vulnerability, and radical self-love. Take one breath, one step, and one choice at a time.

EXERCISE: EXPLORING PERSONAL SPACE

This practice is designed to enhance your awareness of the boundaries around your personal space. By cultivating a tangible felt sense of your energetic field, you can develop a clearer understanding of your needs for safety, comfort, and connection. Regularly attuning to your spatial boundaries can support healthier relationships and more effective self-protection. Approach this exercise with a spirit of open curiosity, noticing the subtle sensations and emotions that arise as you explore the edges of your personal space.

Guided Instructions

1. Begin by finding an open area where you can move around freely. This might be a room in your home, a private outdoor space, or a quiet corner of a park.

2. Take a few grounding breaths, bringing your awareness inward. Notice any sensations, emotions, or thoughts that are present without judgment.

3. Now, extend your awareness outward, sensing the energetic field that surrounds your body. You might imagine this as a bubble or aura that extends a few feet in all directions.

4. Slowly begin to walk around space, maintaining awareness of this energetic boundary. Notice how it moves with you as if you are carrying a protective shield.

5. Experiment by stepping just outside of your intuitive boundary, then back inside. Notice any shifts in your bodily sensations, emotions, or overall sense of comfort as you cross this threshold.

6. Play with expanding and contracting the size of your energetic field. Make it smaller, as if you are drawing your boundaries in close. Then, gradually expand it outward, as if you are creating more spaciousness around you.

7. As you explore these different sizes of personal space, notice any patterns or preferences that

emerge. Do you feel more at ease with a larger or smaller energetic field? Are there certain areas of your body that feel more sensitive to boundary violations?

8. If you have a trusted partner and feel comfortable doing so, you can explore this practice in a relationship. Stand a good distance apart, then have your partner slowly approach your energetic boundary. Notice the precise moment when you sense them entering your field, as well as any accompanying sensations or emotions.

9. If desired, practice giving voice to your needs around personal space. You might say, "This feels comfortable," or "I need a little more distance." Notice how it feels to clearly communicate your boundaries.

10. As you complete the practice, take a moment to tune into your overall sense of spatial awareness. Notice any shifts in your felt sense of safety, grounding, or relational clarity.

Closing

Take a moment to appreciate your innate capacity to sense and communicate your needs around personal space. Acknowledge any insights or challenges that arose during the practice with a spirit of self-compassion. Consider integrating this boundary awareness exercise into your daily life, perhaps taking a few moments each morning to attune to your energetic field or practicing in real-time as you navigate social interactions. Trust that each time you honor your spatial needs, you are reinforcing patterns of self-care, safety, and authenticity. Carry this felt a sense of healthy boundaries with you as you move through your day, knowing that you have the right to protect and define your personal space.

EXERCISE: SETTING AND MAINTAINING BOUNDARIES

This practice is designed to help you develop embodied boundary-setting skills. By learning to communicate your needs and comfort zones from a place of somatic awareness, you can more effectively advocate for yourself in relationships. Setting clear, consistent boundaries is an empowering act of self-respect that is vital for healthy connections with others. Approach this exercise with a spirit of curiosity and self-compassion, knowing that boundary work is an ongoing process of learning and growth.

Guided Instructions

1. Begin by finding an upright, grounded posture. You might stand with your feet hip-width apart or sit with your sit bones rooted into the chair. Feel a sense of stability and confidence in your body.

2. Take a few calming breaths, allowing yourself to settle into the present moment. Notice any sensations, emotions, or thoughts that arise without judgment.

3. Recall a situation where you need to set a boundary. This might be a real-life scenario or a

hypothetical one. If it is hypothetical, clearly define the context and the specific boundary you want to practice setting.

4. Allow yourself to contact your feelings around this boundary need. Notice any physical sensations that arise, such as tightness in your chest, butterflies in your stomach, or heat in your face. Acknowledge these sensations with compassion.

5. Now, explore embodied ways to communicate your boundary:

   a. Tone of Voice: Experiment with speaking in a firm, clear, and warm tone. Practice statements like, "I need..." or "It's important to me that..." Notice how different vocal qualities feel in your body.

   b. Body Language: Play with nonverbal cues that reinforce your boundary, such as direct eye contact, open and confident gestures, and maintaining an appropriate distance. Notice how these postures impact your sense of power and security.

   c. Verbal Statements: Craft clear, specific boundary statements using "I" language. For example, "I'm not comfortable with..." or "I need you to respect my privacy around..." Avoid blaming or shaming the other person; focus on expressing your own needs.

6. If you feel comfortable, practice physically acting out your boundary communication. Stand up and deliver your statements with the embodied tone and posture you explored. Notice how it feels to give voice and form to your needs.

7. Throughout the exercise, keep returning to your grounded, embodied presence. If you notice yourself getting tense or anxious, take a few breaths and re-center yourself in your body. Remember, setting boundaries is a skill that takes practice and patience.

8. As you complete the exercise, take a moment to acknowledge yourself for the vulnerability and courage it takes to assert your boundaries. Notice any shifts in your sense of self-respect, empowerment, or relational clarity.

Closing
Take a moment to appreciate your innate right to set boundaries and to have those boundaries respected. Honor any challenges or discomfort that arose during the practice, knowing that boundary work often involves moving through fears of confrontation or disappointment. Consider integrating this embodied boundary-setting practice into your daily life, perhaps mentally rehearsing before a difficult conversation or practicing in low-stakes interactions to build confidence. Trust that each time you communicate your needs from a place of somatic awareness, you are deepening your capacity for self-advocacy and relational authenticity. Carry this sense of empowered presence with you as you navigate your relationships, knowing that you have the skills and the strength to set clear, compassionate boundaries.

EXERCISE: ASSERTIVE COMMUNICATION PRACTICE

This practice is designed to help you build skills for assertive self-expression. Assertiveness involves clearly and confidently communicating your needs, boundaries, and perspectives while respecting those of others. This exercise offers an opportunity to give voice to your authentic desires in an empowered way. Remember, assertive communication is a vital part of healthy relating, as it enables you to advocate for yourself and navigate relationships with clarity and integrity.

Guided Instructions

1. Begin by finding an embodied stance that feels both grounded and open. Stand with your feet firmly planted, your shoulders relaxed, and your spine tall. Feel a sense of balance and centeredness in your posture.

2. Take a few deep breaths, allowing yourself to settle into the present moment. Bring to mind a real-life situation where you need to communicate assertively. This might involve expressing a boundary, making a request, or stating a preference.

3. As you connect with this scenario, explore different tones of voice you might use to express yourself:

   a. Practice speaking with clarity and directness but without aggression or harshness. Aim for a tone that is firm yet respectful.

   b. Experiment with infusing your voice with self-assured vigor, avoiding any hints of tentativeness or apology. Remember, your needs and opinions are valid and worthy of expression.

4. Allow any emotions that arise around the situation to be acknowledged and voiced appropriately. You might say, "I feel frustrated when..." or "I'm concerned about..." Naming your emotions can help clarify your perspective and foster empathy in the listener.

5. Now, practice saying your assertive statements out loud, as if the person you need to communicate with is present. Use "I" language and focus on facts rather than judgments. For example, "I need more advance notice when plans change" instead of "You're always inconsiderate."

6. As you speak, pay attention to any tension or constriction in your body. If you notice tightness in your jaw, throat, or chest, take a moment to breathe deeply and consciously relax those areas. Maintaining an open, relaxed posture can help you communicate with greater ease and impact.

7.   If you feel comfortable, engage in a role-playing scenario with a friend or therapist to practice your assertive communication. Take turns being the speaker and the listener, offering each other feedback and support.

8.   Throughout the practice, keep returning to your centered, grounded presence. If you find yourself getting anxious or defensive, take a few breaths and reconnect with your embodied sense of stability and strength.

Closing

As you complete this practice, please take a moment to acknowledge yourself for the courage and vulnerability it takes to express yourself assertively. Notice any shifts in your sense of empowerment, self-respect, or relational ease. Consider integrating assertive communication practice into your daily life, perhaps starting with low-stakes situations and gradually building up to more challenging conversations. Remember, assertiveness is a skill that deepens with repetition and self-reflection. Trust that each time you give voice to your authentic needs and boundaries, you are strengthening your capacity for healthy, fulfilling relationships—with others and with yourself.

EXERCISE: BREATH-GUIDED BOUNDARY AFFIRMATIONS

Breath-Guided Boundary Affirmations is an exercise that combines the power of positive affirmations with the grounding and centering practice of diaphragmatic breathing. This exercise invites you to use your breath as an anchor for repeating and internalizing key phrases that affirm your right to set boundaries, communicate your needs, and protect your well-being. By synchronizing your affirmations with your breath, you can cultivate a deeper sense of embodiment, self-worth, and emotional regulation. Regular practice of this exercise can help you develop a more positive and empowered mindset around boundaries and navigate challenging situations with greater clarity, calm, and self-compassion.

Steps

1. Find a quiet, comfortable space where you can sit without distraction. Choose a chair or cushion that allows you to maintain a straight but relaxed spine with your feet flat on the floor.

2. Close your eyes and take a few deep breaths, allowing your body to settle and your mind to become present. Notice the natural flow of your breath, the rise and fall of your chest and belly.

3. Begin to deepen and slow your breath, inhaling through your nose and exhaling through your mouth. Aim for a smooth, steady rhythm, with each inhale and exhale lasting about 4-6 seconds.

4. As you continue to breathe, silently repeat the following affirmations in sync with your breath:

- On the inhale, think to yourself: "I have the right to set boundaries."

- On the exhale, think to yourself: "I communicate my needs with clarity and respect."

Repeat this affirmation pair for several rounds of breath, allowing the words to sink deep into your body and mind.

5. After a few minutes, switch to a new pair of affirmations:

- On the inhale, think to yourself: "I honor my limits and capacity."
- On the exhale, think to yourself: "I protect my time, energy, and well-being."

Again, repeat this pair for several rounds of breath, focusing on the meaning and intention behind each phrase.

6. Continue cycling through different boundary affirmations, spending a few minutes with each pair. Some other examples include:

- Inhale: "I trust my intuition and inner wisdom."
- Exhale: "I make choices that align with my values and goals."

- Inhale: "I am worthy of love, respect, and understanding."
- Exhale: "I surround myself with people who honor my boundaries."

- Inhale: "I release guilt, shame, and people-pleasing tendencies."
- Exhale: "I stand firm in my truth and my right to self-care."

Feel free to create affirmations that resonate with your specific needs and challenges.

7. As you repeat each affirmation, notice any sensations, emotions, or thoughts that arise. If you find your mind wandering or resisting the affirmations, gently redirect your attention back to your breath and the words you are repeating.

8. After 10-15 minutes of breath-guided affirmations, take a few deep breaths and sit in silence for a moment. Notice any shifts in your energy, mood, or sense of self-empowerment.

9. Gently open your eyes and return to your surroundings. Take a moment to journal about your experience, reflecting on which affirmations resonated most strongly and how you can apply them in your daily life.

10. As you move through your day, look for opportunities to practice your boundary affirmations in real-life situations. Remember that, like any skill, asserting boundaries becomes easier and more natural with repetition and self-compassion.

Conclusion

Breath-Guided Boundary Affirmations were included in this book because it offers a simple but effective way to reprogram your mind and body for healthier, more assertive boundary setting. By combining the neurological benefits of affirmations with the physiological benefits of diaphragmatic breathing, this exercise helps you cultivate a deeper sense of self-worth, emotional regulation, and interpersonal effectiveness. Regular practice can help you overcome people-pleasing tendencies, communicate your needs more confidently, and make choices that honor your authentic self. Ultimately, Breath-Guided Boundary Affirmations is a tool for claiming your right to safety, respect, and well-being in all areas of your life.

EXERCISE: EMBODIED BOUNDARY SETTING WITH PMR

Embodied Boundary Setting with Progressive Muscle Relaxation is an exercise that combines the physical practice of progressive muscle relaxation (PMR) with the psychological practice of boundary setting. This exercise invites you to explore the felt sense of boundaries in your body, using the tool of PMR to release tension and cultivate a sense of safety, strength, and assertiveness. By physically embodying different boundary scenarios and practicing relaxation techniques, you can develop greater confidence and skill in communicating your needs and limits in real-life situations. Regular practice of this exercise can help you navigate challenging relationships with greater ease, maintain healthier personal and professional boundaries, and feel more empowered and resilient in the face of stress or conflict.

Steps

1. Find a quiet, private space where you can sit or lie down comfortably. If sitting, choose a chair that supports your back and allows your feet to rest flat on the floor. If lying down, use a mat or blanket for padding.

2. Close your eyes and take a few deep breaths, allowing your body to settle and your mind to become present. Notice any areas of tension or discomfort in your body, and imagine your breath flowing into those areas, softening and releasing any tightness.

3. Now, bring to mind a recent or upcoming situation in which you need to set a boundary or communicate a limit. This could be saying no to an unreasonable request, asserting your needs in a relationship, or protecting your time and energy in a work setting.

4. As you imagine this scenario, notice any physical sensations that arise in your body. You may feel tension in your jaw, tightness in your chest, or a knot in your stomach. Take a moment to observe these sensations with curiosity and compassion.

5. Now, begin the PMR practice by tensing and relaxing each muscle group in your body, starting with your feet and moving upward. As you tense each muscle group, imagine yourself setting the boundary or communicating the limit in a clear, confident, and assertive way.

6. For example, as you tense your feet and legs, imagine yourself standing firm and grounded in your boundary. As you tense your stomach and chest, imagine your voice coming from a place of strength and conviction. As you tense your jaw and face, imagine maintaining eye contact and a neutral, composed expression.

7. After tensing each muscle group for 5-10 seconds, release the tension and imagine any stress, fear, or doubt draining out of your body. Notice the sense of relief and empowerment that comes from letting go of tension and standing in your truth.

8. Move through the body, tensing and relaxing each muscle group in turn: feet and legs, hips and buttocks, stomach and lower back, chest and upper back, arms and hands, neck and shoulders, face and jaw. Take your time and focus on the physical sensations and imaginative prompts associated with each area.

9. Once you have completed the PMR sequence, take a few deep breaths and notice how your body feels. Observe any shifts in your energy, confidence, or emotional state. Notice any new insights or strategies that have emerged for handling the boundary situation.

10. When you feel ready, gently open your eyes and return to your surroundings. Take a moment to journal about your experience, reflecting on what you learned about your boundaries, your body, and your ability to assert yourself.

11. As you move forward, look for opportunities to practice embodied boundary setting in your daily life. Remember that setting boundaries is a skill that gets stronger with practice and that your body is a powerful ally in communicating your needs and limits.

Conclusion

Embodied Boundary Setting with Progressive Muscle Relaxation was included in this book because it offers a holistic approach to developing assertiveness, self-respect, and interpersonal effectiveness. By combining the physical practice of PMR with the psychological practice of boundary setting, this exercise helps you cultivate a felt sense of safety, strength, and empowerment in your body. Regular practice can help you communicate your needs more clearly, handle challenging relationships more skillfully, and maintain healthier personal and professional boundaries. Ultimately, Embodied Boundary Setting is a tool for honoring your worth and well-being while building more authentic and respectful connections with others.

11. WORKING WITH BODY ARMOR AND CHRONIC TENSION

In the journey of embodied healing, exploring body armor and chronic tension is a profound and transformative area of work. These are the places in our physical form where we hold the imprints of stress, trauma, and overwhelming experiences, where our body has shaped itself around pain and fear to protect and defend us.

Many of us have become so accustomed to these patterns of armoring and tension that we hardly notice them anymore, feeling like they are a normal part of who we are. We may walk through the world with hunched shoulders, clenched jaws, and tight bellies without questioning why or how these patterns came to be.

In somatic therapy, we recognize these areas of chronic holding as powerful messengers from the depths of our being, expressing our unresolved wounds, unmet needs, and unintegrated experiences. By learning to listen to them with curiosity, compassion, and care, we open a doorway to profound healing and transformation.

UNDERSTANDING BODY ARMOR

The concept of body armor, coined by psychoanalyst Wilhelm Reich, suggests that chronic patterns of muscular tension correlate with psychological defenses and emotional blocks. When we experience stress, trauma, or intense emotion, our body responds by contracting, tightening, and bracing to manage the overwhelming energy and sensation. Suppose these experiences are not fully processed and integrated. In that case, the body may continue to hold these tension patterns long after the original threat has passed, creating chronic armoring that restricts breath, movement, and vitality.

Common areas of body armoring include the jaw and throat (unexpressed anger, grief, fear), shoulders and neck (stress and overwhelm), chest and heart area (heartbreak or betrayal), belly and diaphragm (shame or powerlessness), and pelvis and lower back (sexual trauma or violation). Each person's patterns of holding are unique to their history, temperament, and experience. Still, all forms of armoring represent a somatic attempt to protect and defend the self from further harm or overwhelm.

Body armor is intimately linked to our psychological defenses—mental and emotional strategies we use to cope with stress, conflict, or threat. While these patterns may have served us in the past, they often limit us in the present, restricting our breath, movement, and expression, keeping us stuck in chronic tension and vigilance, and disconnecting us from the natural flow and aliveness of our embodied experience.

SOFTENING BODY ARMORING

The body has a remarkable capacity for softening, releasing, and letting go, just as it has for armoring itself in the face of threat. With patience, presence, and skilled support, even the most chronic patterns of tension can begin to unwind, revealing new possibilities for ease, flow, and vitality.

In somatic therapy, approaches to working with body armor and chronic tension include gentle, mindful touch to build trust, safety, and attunement between the client and their embodied experience and titration—working with intense sensation or emotion in small, manageable doses. Therapists guide clients to develop awareness and trust in areas of holding, exploring subtle movements and expressions while staying attuned to the nervous system and creating a sense of safety and containment.

As layers of body armor soften and unwind, approaching the process with self-compassion and care is crucial. These holding patterns developed over time and deserve to be honored and respected as we work to release and transform them. Affirmative self-talk or mantras can help cultivate self-compassion and rewire the nervous system, creating new pathways of self-love and self-trust.

The journey of softening body armor is a journey of coming home to ourselves, reclaiming the fullness and vibrancy of our embodied experience. It requires patience, persistence, and a willingness to sit with discomfort and uncertainty but offers profound rewards—feeling more alive, connected, and at peace in our skin.

EXERCISE: IDENTIFYING YOUR BODY ARMOR PATTERNS

Body armoring refers to chronic patterns of muscular tension and bracing that develop in response to stress, trauma, or psychological defenses. Often unconscious, these patterns of holding serve as a type of protective "armor," altering our posture, movement, and breathing. By becoming aware of your unique body armor patterns, you create opportunities for release, healing, and a return to more organic ways of being in your body. Approach this practice with a spirit of gentle curiosity and self-compassion.

Guided Instructions
1. Begin by finding a comfortable posture, either seated or lying down. Ensure that your body feels supported and at ease.

2. Take a few slow, grounding breaths, allowing your awareness to settle into your body. Notice the weight of your form contacting the surface beneath you.

3. Now, guide your attention through a mindful body scan, starting at your feet and gradually moving up to the crown of your head.

4. As you scan each area, tune in any sensations of gripping, tightness, or bracing. You might notice tension in your jaw, a sense of held breath in your chest, or a feeling of armoring in your belly.

5. When you discover an area of holding, pause and bring your full, compassionate attention to the sensation. Acknowledge the tension without trying to change it.

6. Get curious about this pattern of armoring. When do you first remember experiencing this type of holding? What purpose might it have served in your life? What circumstances or emotions tend to trigger or intensify it?

7. If it feels safe and appropriate, allow any emotions, memories, or imagery associated with the armoring to arise. Notice how the physical sensation might be connected to your psychological experience.

8. Experiment with consciously intensifying the tension for a moment, then releasing it. Notice if the armoring softens or shifts in response to your mindful attention.

9. Remember to stay present and grounded throughout the practice. If any strong emotions or sensations arise, take a pause and re-center yourself with a few slow breaths. Trust your body's wisdom, and do not force any release that isn't ready to happen.

10. Continue scanning through your body, identifying and exploring any other areas of chronic holding. If you like, you can make notes or a simple sketch of your body armor patterns to refer to.

Closing

As you complete this practice, please take a moment to appreciate your body's innate intelligence and the ways it has sought to protect you through patterns of armoring. Offer gratitude and compassion to your younger self, who may have first developed these tensions as a way to cope with overwhelming experiences. Consider making this type of body armor inquiry a regular part of your self-care routine, perhaps journaling about your insights or sharing them with a trusted therapist or friend. Remember, bringing awareness to our patterns is the first step in creating space for new possibilities. Trust that each time you meet your body with curious, loving attention, you are planting seeds of release, resilience, and deep somatic healing.

EXERCISE: SOFTENING AND RELEASING CHRONIC TENSION

This practice offers a gentle, safe way to release patterns of habitual gripping and bracing in the body. By consciously softening areas of chronic tension, you create space for new embodied experiences of ease, flexibility, and flow. Remember, letting go of long-held tension requires patience, kindness, and a willingness to go slowly. Trust that your body has its wisdom and timeline for release, and approach this practice as a loving dialogue rather than a forceful intervention.

Guided Instructions

1. Begin by finding a comfortable posture, either seated or lying down. Ensure that your body feels well-supported and at ease.

2. Take a few slow, calming breaths, allowing your awareness to settle into your physical form. Notice the weight of your body contacting the surface beneath you.

3. Gently give your attention to areas where you typically hold chronic tension. This might include your jaw, shoulders, chest, belly, or hips.

4. Start by softening the muscles of your face and jaw. Unclench your teeth, relax your brow, and let your tongue rest heavily in your mouth. Imagine your facial bones gently widening and your ears floating away from each other.

5. On your next exhale, imagine the breath moving down through your body like a wave, inviting each tense area to gently soften and release.

6. You might layer in some gentle somatic movements to support this unwinding process. Slowly and mindfully, turn your head from side to side, circle your shoulders, or rock your hips. Let these movements be organic and unstructured, following the natural impulses of your body.

7. As you continue to breathe and move, notice any areas that feel resistant to releasing. Acknowledge this tension with compassion, reminding yourself that it has served a protective purpose. Imagine sending breath and kindness to these areas without demand or expectation.

8. If at any point you feel overwhelmed or disconnected, pause and resource yourself with longer exhales or self-nurturing touch. Place a hand on your heart, give yourself a gentle hug, or cup your face with your palms. These gestures of self-love can help regulate your nervous system and restore a sense of safety.

9. Remember, the goal is not to force your body into a state of complete relaxation. Rather, it is to introduce the possibility of ease and to cultivate a relationship of trust and attunement with your physical self.

10. As you complete the practice, take a few moments to rest in stillness, noticing any shifts in your embodied experience. Observe your breath, your heartbeat, and the sensations that arise in the spaciousness you have created.

Closing

As you finish this practice, take a moment to appreciate your body's innate capacity for release and renewal. Honor the courage it takes to let go of familiar patterns and to trust in the wisdom of your soma. Consider integrating this type of gentle unwinding into your daily routine, perhaps as a morning or bedtime ritual. Remember, softening chronic tension is a gradual, nonlinear process that requires consistent, loving attention. Trust that each time you meet your body with compassionate presence, you are nourishing the seeds of deep, lasting transformation.

EXERCISE: DEVELOPING SELF-COMPASSION FOR YOUR BODY

This practice is designed to cultivate an attitude of kindness and understanding toward your body. In a culture that often encourages self-judgment and criticism, embodying self-compassion can be a radical act of healing. By meeting your physical form with tender awareness and care, you create the conditions for deeper mind-body integration and wholeness. Remember, developing self-compassion is a gentle, gradual process that requires patience and a willingness to soften habitual patterns of harshness.

Guided Instructions

1. Begin by finding a comfortable posture, either seated or lying down. Ensure that your body feels well-supported and at ease.

2. Take a few slow, calming breaths, allowing your awareness to settle into the present moment. Notice the sensations of your breath moving in and out and the weight of your body contacting the surface beneath you.

3. Now, guide your attention through a gentle body scan, starting at the crown of your head and moving down to the soles of your feet. As you scan each area, notice the physical sensations that are present without trying to change or judge them.

4. If you encounter any areas of tension, discomfort, or resistance, pause and bring your full, tender awareness to the sensation. Imagine cradling this part of your body with deep care and understanding, as you might hold a small child or a beloved pet.

5. Silently or aloud, offer compassionate statements to your body, acknowledging its challenges and its resilience. You might say something like, "I know you are carrying so much, dear body. I honor your struggles and your courage."

6. Explore placing a hand on your heart, belly, or any area that needs extra kindness. Let your touch be soft and soothing, conveying a message of safety and acceptance. You might gently stroke or pat this area as if comforting a dear friend.

7. Imagine warmth and care flowing through your entire body, like a nurturing bath or a soft, enveloping light. Allow this energy of compassion to penetrate every cell, every tissue, every space within you.

8. If you notice any blocks or resistance to receiving this kindness, acknowledge them with understanding. Remind yourself that it is natural to struggle with self-compassion, given the messages of self-criticism that are so prevalent in our world.

9. Keep returning to the practice of offering tender awareness and care to your body in whatever way feels authentic and nourishing to you. Trust that even the smallest gestures of self-compassion can

have a profound ripple effect on your overall well-being.

10. As you complete the practice, take a few moments to rest in the afterglow of this self-care. Notice any shifts in your embodied experience and any softening of the boundaries between mind and body.

Closing

As you finish this practice, take a moment to appreciate your willingness to meet your body with compassion and care. Acknowledge the courage it takes to soften the armor of self-judgment and embrace your physical form with tender acceptance. Consider integrating this type of self-compassion exercise into your daily routine, perhaps as a morning or bedtime ritual. Remember, each moment of kindness toward your body is planting seeds of self-love and interoceptive attunement that will blossom over time. Trust in the transformative power of self-compassion and your innate capacity for embodied wholeness and ease

EXERCISE: PROGRESSIVE MUSCLE RELAXATION FOR BODY ARMOR RELEASE

Progressive Muscle Relaxation for Body Armor Release is an exercise that combines the technique of progressive muscle relaxation (PMR) with the concept of body armor, or chronic patterns of muscular tension and holding. This exercise invites you to systematically tense and relax different muscle groups while also bringing awareness to areas of the body where you tend to hold stress, anxiety, or emotional pain. By intentionally tensing and releasing these areas of body armor, you can start to break up patterns of chronic tension, promote deeper relaxation, and cultivate a greater sense of safety and ease in your body. Regular practice of this exercise can help you develop a more balanced and harmonious relationship between your mind and body, even in the face of life's challenges and stressors.

Steps

1. Find a quiet, comfortable place where you can lie down or sit without distraction. If lying down, use a mat or blanket for padding, and support your head and knees with pillows if needed. If sitting, choose a chair that allows your feet to rest flat on the floor and your spine to be straight but not rigid.

2. Close your eyes and take a few deep breaths, allowing your body to settle and your mind to become present. Notice the weight of your body on the surface beneath you and the sensation of your breath moving in and out.

3. Starting with your feet and toes, gently tense the muscles in this area, scrunching your toes and contracting the soles of your feet. Hold this tension for 5-10 seconds, noticing the sensation of tightness and contraction.

4. Now, exhale and release the tension, allowing your feet and toes to relax completely. Notice the sensation of letting go and the contrast between tension and relaxation.

5. Move your attention up to your lower legs and calves, and repeat the process of tensing and relaxing. As you release the tension, imagine any stress or holding in this area melting away.

6. Continue moving up through your body, systematically tensing and relaxing each muscle group:

- Thighs and buttocks
- Hips and pelvis
- Stomach and lower back
- Chest and upper back
- Shoulders and neck
- Arms and hands
- Face (forehead, eyes, cheeks, jaw, and mouth)

7. As you tense each muscle group, notice any areas that feel particularly tight or armored. Acknowledge these areas with curiosity and compassion, and as you release the tension, imagine the breath moving into these areas, inviting a sense of softness and ease.

8. If you notice any emotions or memories arising as you work with particular areas of body armor, allow them to be present without judgment. Breathe into these experiences, and imagine them releasing and dissolving as you exhale.

9. After completing the PMR sequence, take a few deep breaths and notice the overall state of relaxation in your body. Acknowledge any areas that feel more relaxed or open, and set an intention to bring this sense of ease and release into your daily life.

10. Gently open your eyes and take a moment to reorient to your surroundings. Notice any shifts in your body or mind after completing the exercise.

11. As you move through your day, see if you can maintain a sense of connection to the relaxed, open state you cultivated during the practice. If you notice areas of tension or armoring arising, take a few deep breaths and imagine releasing and softening those areas.

Conclusion

Progressive Muscle Relaxation for Body Armor Release was included in this book because it offers a structured, systematic way to work with patterns of chronic tension and holding in the body. By combining the proven technique of PMR with mindful attention to areas of body armor, this exercise can help you develop a deeper understanding of your unique patterns of stress and tension and cultivate the skills to release and soften these patterns over time. Regular practice of this exercise can lead to greater physical comfort, emotional resilience, and a more peaceful and harmonious relationship between mind and body. With patience and persistence, Progressive Muscle Relaxation for Body Armor Release can be a powerful tool for enhancing embodiment self-regulation.

EXERCISE: BREATH-GUIDED BODY ARMOR SOFTENING

Breath-Guided Body Armor Softening is an exercise that combines diaphragmatic breathing with mindful attention to areas of chronic tension or "body armor" in order to promote relaxation, release, and a greater sense of ease and openness in the body. This practice invites you to use your breath as a gentle, soothing tool to explore and soften areas of holding or bracing, cultivating a more compassionate and accepting relationship with your physical experience. By bringing conscious breath and awareness to patterns of tension, you can start to unwind deep-seated patterns of stress and anxiety and develop a greater sense of safety, resilience, and embodied presence. Regular practice of Breath-Guided Body Armor Softening can help you feel more at home in your body, even in the face of life's challenges and difficulties.

Steps

1. Find a quiet, comfortable place where you can sit or lie down without distraction. If sitting, choose a position that allows your spine to be straight but not rigid and your feet to rest flat on the floor. If lying down, use a mat or blanket for padding, and support your head and knees with pillows if needed.

2. Close your eyes and take a few deep breaths, allowing your body to settle and your mind to become present. Notice the sensation of your breath moving in and out of your body and the gentle rise and fall of your belly with each inhale and exhale.

3. Bring your attention to your body and notice any areas that feel tense, tight, or armored. These may be areas where you habitually hold stress or anxiety, such as your jaw, shoulders, chest, or belly. Acknowledge these areas with curiosity and kindness without trying to change them.

4. Begin to deepen and slow your breath, focusing on breathing into your belly and lower rib cage. Imagine each inhale gently expanding and softening any areas of tension or holding and each exhale inviting a sense of release and letting go.

5. As you continue to breathe deeply and slowly, bring your attention to one of the areas of body armor you identified. Imagine directing your breath into this area as if the breath could gently massage and soothe any tension or tightness.

6. With each inhale, imagine the breath creating space and openness in this area, and exhale, imagine any tension or holding gently melting away. You may want to visualize the breath as a warm, calming light or energy, slowly dissolving any armor or protective layers.

7. Take your time with each area of body armor, using the breath to gently explore and soften any sensations of tightness or bracing. If you notice any emotions or memories arising as you work with a particular area, acknowledge them with compassion and invite them to be released with each exhale.

8. After spending a few minutes with each area of body armor, take a few deep breaths and notice the overall state of your body. Observe any shifts in sensation, energy, or perception that may have

occurred through this practice.

9. As you prepare to end the practice, set an intention to bring this sense of breath-guided softening and release into your daily life. Whenever you notice areas of tension or holding arising, remember that you can use your breath as a gentle, soothing tool to promote relaxation and ease.

10. Gently open your eyes and take a moment to reorient to your surroundings. Notice any changes in your body or state of mind, and take a few moments to appreciate your practice.

Conclusion

Breath-Guided Body Armor Softening was included in this book because it offers a simple yet powerful way to work with patterns of chronic tension and holding in the body. By using the breath as a gentle, nourishing tool to explore and soften areas of body armor, this practice can help you develop a more compassionate and accepting relationship with your physical experience, even in the face of discomfort or difficulty. Regular practice of Breath-Guided Body Armor Softening can help you release deep-seated patterns of stress and anxiety, cultivate greater resilience and adaptability, and promote a sense of embodied presence and well-being. With time and patience, this practice can be a valuable resource for anyone seeking to feel more at home and ease in their body and their life.

EXERCISE: HEART-CENTERED BODY ARMOR COMPASSION PRACTICE

Heart-Centered Body Armor Compassion Practice is an exercise that combines heart rate variability biofeedback (HRVB) with mindful self-compassion to help you soften and release patterns of chronic tension or "body armor." This practice invites you to connect with the wisdom and compassion of your heart, using the feedback from your HRVB device to cultivate a state of coherence and emotional balance as you offer kindness and understanding to areas of holding or bracing in your body. By bringing a heart-centered, compassionate awareness to patterns of tension, you can start to unwind deep-seated patterns of stress and self-judgment and develop a greater sense of safety, acceptance, and embodied presence. Regular practice of Heart-Centered Body Armor Compassion can help you cultivate a more loving and harmonious relationship with your body and your whole self.

Steps

1. Begin by finding a quiet, comfortable space where you can sit without distraction. Attach your HRVB device according to the manufacturer's instructions, ensuring that the sensor is properly placed on your finger or earlobe.

2. Sit in a comfortable position, with your feet flat on the floor and your spine straight but relaxed. Take a few deep breaths, allowing your body to settle and your mind to become present.

3. Turn on your HRVB device and begin monitoring your heart rate variability. Most devices will provide feedback through a visual display or audio cues, helping you track your level of coherence

and emotional balance.

4. As you continue to breathe deeply and evenly, bring your attention to your heart center in the middle of your chest. Imagine that with each inhale, you are drawing in a sense of love, compassion, and acceptance for yourself and your body. With each exhale, imagine releasing any self-judgment, criticism, or resistance.

5. Once you feel connected to your heart and its compassionate energy, bring your awareness to your body and notice any areas that feel tense, tight, or armored. These may be areas where you habitually hold stress, anxiety, or self-judgment, such as your jaw, shoulders, chest, or belly.

6. Choose one area of body armor to focus on, and imagine directing your heart-centered compassion and understanding to this area. Silently offer phrases of kindness and acceptance to this part of your body, such as "I see you," "I'm here with you," or "I accept you as you are."

7. As you offer these phrases of compassion, notice if there are any shifts in your HRVB feedback. See if you can find a way of relating to your body armor that feels both kind and coherent, adjusting your inner tone until you find a balance of warmth and equanimity.

8. Continue to breathe into the area of body armor, imagining the breath gently softening and soothing any tension or holding. With each exhale, imagine any pain, fear, or resistance being released with compassion and understanding.

9. Take your time with each area of body armor, offering it the heartfelt compassion and acceptance it may have been longing for. If you notice any emotions or memories arising as you work with a particular area, meet them with the same kindness and care you are offering your body.

10. After spending a few minutes with each area of body armor, take a few deep breaths and notice the overall state of your body and heart. Observe any shifts in sensation, emotion, or perception that may have occurred through this practice.

11. As you prepare to end the practice, take a moment to appreciate your courage and willingness to be present with your body's experience. Set an intention to bring this heart-centered compassion and acceptance into your daily life, meeting yourself and others with greater kindness and care.

12. Gently remove your HRVB device and take a few moments to sit in silence, integrating the benefits of your practice. When you feel ready, slowly open your eyes and return to your day, carrying the warmth and wisdom of your heart with you.

Conclusion

Heart-Centered Body Armor Compassion Practice was included in this book because it offers a powerful way to bring the transformative qualities of self-compassion and heart-centered awareness to the process of releasing chronic tension and armoring in the body. By combining the principles of HRVB with mindful self-compassion, this practice can help you develop a more loving and accepting relationship with your embodied experience, even in the face of discomfort or difficulty.

Regular practice of Heart-Centered Body Armor Compassion can help you soften patterns of self-judgment and resistance, cultivate greater emotional resilience and adaptability, and promote a sense of wholeness and integration between your mind, body, and heart. With time and dedication, this practice can be a profound resource for anyone seeking to live with greater ease, authenticity, and self-acceptance.

PART IV: SOMATIC TOOLS FOR STRESS AND TRAUMA

INTEGRATING TRAUMA WITH TITRATION TECHNIQUES

One of the cornerstone principles of working with trauma somatically is the concept of titration. Titration refers to the process of gradually exposing oneself to small, manageable doses of activation related to traumatic material. This approach is crucial in preventing re-traumatization and allowing the nervous system to slowly build tolerance and resilience.

Titration techniques emphasize the importance of developing a robust foundation of resources and coping strategies before engaging with the deeper layers of traumatic experience. By cultivating a felt sense of safety, grounding, and self-regulation, we create a stable base from which to explore and process the more challenging aspects of our healing journey.

Some specific titration techniques include:

- **Pendulation:** This involves allowing the natural oscillation between states of activation and settling, much like the ebb and flow of waves. By gently riding these waves of sensation and emotion, we can develop a greater capacity to tolerate and integrate intense experiences.

- **Resourcing:** Resourcing refers to the practice of intentionally connecting with experiences of safety, support, and nourishment, both within us and in our environment. By regularly accessing and strengthening these resources, we build resilience and counterbalance the destabilizing effects of trauma.

- **Expanding the "window of tolerance":** The window of tolerance represents the optimal zone of arousal where we can effectively process and integrate information. Through titrated exposure and skill-building, we gradually expand this window, increasing our ability to handle more intense or challenging experiences without becoming overwhelmed or shutting down.

Throughout the process of titration, it is essential to respect the body's natural pacing and to resist the urge to force or rush the healing process. Trauma recovery is a highly individualized journey, and what feels safe and manageable for one person may be triggering or overwhelming for another. By honoring our own unique needs and boundaries, we create a foundation of self-compassion and trust that can sustain us through the difficulties of the healing path.

RECOGNIZING HOW TRAUMA LEAVES THE BODY WITH SEQUENCING TOOLS

Trauma leaves a profound impact on the body, often in the form of residual charge and incomplete survival responses. When we experience a threatening or overwhelming situation, our bodies instinctively mobilize to protect us, activating the fight-flight or freeze response. However, when these survival responses are thwarted or unable to be completed, the associated energy and tension can become trapped in the body, leading to a host of physical and emotional symptoms.

Sequencing tools in somatic therapy aim to facilitate the release and completion of these bound survival energies, allowing the body to return to a state of greater regulation and balance. By tracking the natural progression of survival responses, from orientation to fight/flight to freeze and beyond, we can identify where the process may have become stuck or interrupted.

Through gentle exploration of sensation and movement, we can begin to uncover and work with these areas of residual activation. This may involve practices such as:

- Mindfully attending to physical sensations and impulses without judgment or expectation.
- Allowing the body to express itself through spontaneous movements, gestures, or vocalizations.
- Experimenting with small, incremental discharges of tension through shaking, trembling, or other forms of release.

As with titration, it is crucial to approach sequencing work with caution and respect for the body's wisdom and timing. Adequate resourcing and support are essential to prevent re-traumatization, as the process of uncovering and releasing bound survival responses can be intense and destabilizing.

However, when facilitated with skill and care, sequencing practices can be profoundly transformative, supporting greater integration and coherence within the body-mind system. As we learn to listen to and trust the intelligence of our bodies, we open new pathways for healing, growth, and empowerment.

The chapters in this section will guide you through a range of somatic tools and practices for working with stress and trauma, including techniques for building resources, navigating arousal and overwhelm, befriending shame, and healing dissociation. By engaging with these practices in a spirit of curiosity, compassion, and self-attunement, you will develop a deeper understanding of your own embodied experience and a greater capacity for resilience and self-regulation.

PTSD AND C-PTSD

Post-Traumatic Stress Disorder (PTSD) and Complex PTSD (C-PTSD) are debilitating conditions that arise from exposure to traumatic experiences. While PTSD typically develops following a single traumatic event, C-PTSD is associated with prolonged, repeated trauma, often occurring in childhood or situations of captivity. Both conditions involve the traumatic experiences becoming deeply encoded in the body, leading to a wide range of distressing somatic symptoms.

When an individual experiences a traumatic event, their body's natural survival responses of fight, flight, or freeze are activated. If these responses are unable to be completed and resolved, the traumatic energy can become trapped in the body, leading to chronic hyperarousal, intrusive thoughts, flashbacks, and emotional numbness. The body remains in a state of heightened vigilance, constantly scanning for threats and reacting as if the trauma is still occurring in the present.

Traditional talk therapy approaches, which focus primarily on the cognitive and emotional aspects of trauma, can often miss the deeply embedded somatic components. While understanding the narrative of the trauma and processing the associated emotions is important, true healing requires addressing the physiological imprints of trauma stored in the body.

Somatic therapy offers a range of techniques for safely working with the physical activation and dysregulation associated with PTSD and C-PTSD. A key principle is the importance of building resources and stability before delving into the traumatic material. This involves practices such as grounding, centering, and cultivating a felt sense of safety in the body. By establishing a foundation of embodied resilience, individuals can develop the capacity to tolerate and integrate the intense sensations and emotions that may arise during trauma processing.

Another crucial aspect of somatic trauma therapy is the use of pendulation - gently guiding the individual's attention back and forth between the activation of the traumatic material and the regulation of the nervous system. This rhythmic oscillation helps to prevent overwhelming and re-traumatization, allowing the individual to gradually build tolerance for the traumatic sensations while also reinforcing their capacity for self-regulation.

Somatic therapy also works with the body's natural defensive responses that may have been thwarted or incomplete during the original trauma. By providing a safe, controlled space to explore and express these truncated fight, flight or freeze responses, individuals can release the pent-up survival energy and restore a sense of empowerment and control. This may involve techniques such as physically pushing against resistance, vocalization, or engaging in expressive movement.

In addition to these active techniques, somatic therapy also employs more subtle, titrated exposure to the traumatic activation. By gently inviting the body to experience and stay present with small, manageable doses of the traumatic sensations, individuals can begin to desensitize and metabolize the held charge. This gradual exposure allows for the spontaneous release and integration of the traumatic material without triggering excessive overwhelm or dissociation.

Heart Rate Variability Biofeedback (HRVB) is another valuable tool in the somatic treatment of PTSD and C-PTSD. By training individuals to regulate their breath and heart rate coherence, HRVB can help to rewire the nervous system's response to stress and promote greater resilience. Specific HRVB techniques, such as paced breathing coordinated with heart rhythm, can be particularly effective in reducing hyperarousal and restoring a sense of physiological calm and balance.

OTHER SOMATIC PRACTICES THAT CAN SUPPORT THE HEALING OF PTSD AND C-PTSD INCLUDE:

- Tracking bodily sensations and channeling them through movement or creative expression
- Breathing and grounding exercises to help regain and maintain the window of tolerance
- Resourcing and establishing somatic "anchors" of safety, such as a comforting touch or soothing image
- Mindfulness practices to cultivate present-moment awareness and non-reactivity to distressing sensations and emotions

It is important to emphasize that somatic trauma work must be approached with great care and sensitivity. The pacing of the work should be adjusted to the individual's unique needs and capacity, ensuring that they are not re-traumatized in the process. The therapist must continually attune to the client's level of arousal and regulation, providing support and guidance to help them stay within their window of tolerance.

The power of somatic therapy lies in its ability to directly address and reprogram the trauma procedurally stored in the body. By working with the physiological substrates of PTSD and C-PTSD, somatic techniques can help to release the trapped survival energy, restore nervous system regulation, and promote a deep sense of embodied safety and resilience.

The healing that comes from integrating traumatic material through somatic therapy can be profound and transformative. As individuals learn to befriend and inhabit their bodies with greater ease and mastery, they can begin to reclaim a sense of agency, vitality, and wholeness. The once-overwhelming traumatic activation can be metabolized and transformed, freeing up vital energy for growth, connection, and full engagement with life.

12. BUILDING YOUR SOMATIC RESOURCE TOOLKIT

In somatic healing, cultivating embodied resources—positive, nourishing experiences that help us feel safe, grounded, and resilient in the face of stress and trauma—is a powerful tool. These resources are deeply felt, visceral experiences anchored in the wisdom of our bodies, not just mental constructs, or cognitive coping strategies.

Somatic resources build a foundation of felt safety and support within us, serving as inner wellsprings of calm, comfort, and connection that we can draw upon in times of need. While they may seem simple, they hold immense power to transform our relationship to stress, trauma, and overwhelm.

WHAT ARE SOMATIC RESOURCES?

A somatic resource is any positive, embodied experience that helps us feel more grounded, centered, and at ease in our bodies. It is a felt sense of safety, support, or nourishment that we can access and cultivate through mindful attention and practice.

Common examples of somatic resources include:
- Feeling the solid, supportive ground beneath our feet
- Taking slow, deep breaths into our belly
- Placing a hand on our heart and feeling the warmth and gentle pressure
- Giving ourselves a comforting hug or self-massage
- Sensing the flow of energy and aliveness in our body
- Connecting with a memory of a peaceful, beautiful place in nature
- Tuning into the soothing rhythm of a heartbeat or pulse

Somatic resources are primarily felt and experienced in the body rather than thought about or analyzed in the mind. They focus on cultivating presence, attunement, and self-regulation within our embodied being rather than trying to change or fix thoughts and emotions. This is particularly important when stress or trauma compromises our cognitive capacities, making it difficult to think clearly or access usual problem-solving skills. Our body remains a powerful ally and resource, a storehouse of wisdom and resilience we can learn to trust.

Research has shown that cultivating positive embodied experiences can rewire our nervous system over time, installing a deeper sense of resilience and capacity at a core physiological level. By repeatedly accessing and anchoring states of calm, safety, and connection in our bodies, we counterbalance the effects of stress and trauma, building new neural pathways that support overall health and well-being.

DEVELOPING YOUR PERSONAL RESOURCE PRACTICE

To develop a personal toolkit of somatic resources, start by bringing curiosity and exploration to your embodied experience, paying attention to small, subtle moments of ease, comfort, and pleasure available throughout your day.

Notice how your body softens and relaxes in a warm bath or shower or how your breath deepens and expands when you step outside and feel fresh air on your face. Observe the grounding and support from gentle yoga poses or the joy and aliveness from dancing or singing along to your favorite music.

As you attune to these positive experiences, cultivate them more intentionally, bringing mindful attention and savoring each moment. Take extra seconds to feel the warmth and comfort of a cozy blanket around your shoulders or tune into the soothing vibration of a purring cat on your lap. Experiment with different types of self-touch or movement, noticing which ones help you feel more centered, relaxed, and at ease.

Build a repertoire of go-to resources to call upon in moments of stress or overwhelm. Develop a daily practice of taking ground breaths before starting your workday or placing a hand on your heart whenever you feel anxious or upset. Create a special playlist of calming, uplifting music or a collection of inspiring images and quotes that remind you of your strength and resilience.

Approach the cultivation of resources with playfulness, experimentation, and self-compassion. There is no one-size-fits-all approach; the goal is to build a relationship of trust and attunement with your own embodied experience, listening to and honoring your body's unique needs and preferences.

As you deepen your personal resource practice, you may find that you can access states of calm, grounding, and ease more quickly and easily in the face of stress and challenge. You may become less reactive to triggers and stressors, responding with greater flexibility, adaptability, and choice. You may discover a greater sense of confidence, self-trust, and resilience when navigating life's difficulties with grace and skill.

It is important to remember that somatic resources are not a panacea for the deeper wounds of trauma and stress but rather one tool in a larger toolkit of healing and self-care practices. When working with trauma, cultivating resources slowly, gently, and with great care and attunement is crucial, as trauma can leave us feeling profoundly unsafe, disconnected, and overwhelmed in our bodies. The guidance and support of a skilled somatic therapist can be invaluable in helping us titrate and regulate our nervous system as we gradually build our capacity for embodied safety and resilience.

EXERCISE: IDENTIFYING AND ANCHORING RESOURCES

Resources are positive somatic experiences of feeling grounded, calm, safe, or empowered. By consciously identifying and anchoring these resourced states in the body, we can cultivate resilience at a core physiological level. Having ready access to embodied resources supports emotional regulation and helps us navigate challenges with greater ease and stability. In this practice, you will explore your personal resource landscape and develop tools for calling upon these states when needed.

Guided Instructions

1. Begin by finding a relaxed yet poised posture, either sitting or lying down. Ensure that your body feels well-supported and at ease.

2. Take a few calming breaths, allowing your awareness to settle into the present moment. Notice the sensations of your breath moving in and out and the weight of your body contacting the surface beneath you.

3. Now, guide your attention inward, exploring the inner landscape of your body. Notice any areas that feel particularly grounded, spacious, or vitalized. These are your natural somatic resources.

4. Begin to recall times and places where you have felt genuinely resourced - safe, peaceful, empowered, or deeply at ease. These might be memories from childhood, experiences in nature, or moments of connection with loved ones.

5. Choose one of these resource experiences to work with first. Recreate the memory in your mind's eye, engaging all your senses. See the colors and shapes, hear the sounds, feel the textures and sensations.

6. As you re-inhabit this resourced state, notice how it feels in your body. What are the physical sensations associated with this experience? Perhaps you feel a warmth in your chest, a softening in your belly, or a sense of expansiveness in your posture.

7. Consciously absorb this felt sense into your body, as if you are soaking in the essence of the resource. Imagine every cell, every tissue, every organ being infused with this positive energy.

8. To help anchor the resource in your body, you can use a physical gesture or a keyword. For example, you might place a hand on your heart or say a phrase like "safety" or "strength." Repeat this gesture or word a few times, letting it become associated with the embodied sense of the resource.

9. Take a few moments to marinate in the resourced state, letting it settle deeply into your being. Trust that you can call upon this anchor whenever you need to feel more grounded, calm, or empowered.

10. Repeat this process with additional resource experiences, building a diverse catalog of embodied assets. You might imagine these resources as vibrant colors, shimmering lights, or soothing textures

within your body landscape.

Closing

As you complete this practice, take a moment to appreciate the wealth of resources that reside within your own body. These anchors of safety, strength, and ease are always available to you, even during life's challenges. Consider revisiting your resource catalog regularly to reinforce your resilience and build a felt sense of inner abundance. Remember, by tending to your somatic landscape with care and attention, you are cultivating a deep wellspring of embodied support that can nourish you throughout your journey of growth and healing.

EXERCISE: DEVELOPING SOMATIC COHERENCE

Somatic coherence refers to an integrated mind-body state in which our physiological experiences align with our emotional and cognitive processes. When we are somatically coherent, we feel more fully embodied, self-aware, and self-regulated. This practice involves cultivating a deep attunement to your body's signals and allowing space for your authentic experiences to unfold. By bringing your physical sensations, emotions, and thoughts into greater harmony, you can develop a more unified and resilient sense of self.

Guided Instructions

1. Begin by finding a comfortable posture, either seated or lying down. Ensure that your body feels well-supported and at ease.

2. Take a few grounding breaths, allowing your awareness to settle into the present moment. Notice the sensations of your breath moving in and out and the weight of your body contacting the surface beneath you.

3. Now, guide your attention through a gentle body scan, starting at the crown of your head and moving down to the soles of your feet. As you scan each area, notice the physical sensations that are present without trying to change or judge them.

4. Pay particular attention to any areas of physiological activation or bracing, such as tension in your jaw, tightness in your chest, or a sense of holding in your belly. These are often signs of unprocessed emotional experiences.

5. As you acknowledge these areas of holding, allow the corresponding emotions and thoughts to emerge. What feelings are associated with this physical tension? What beliefs or stories might be contributing to this pattern of bracing?

6. Breathe fully into these experiences, creating space for them to be felt and expressed. You might imagine your breath gently softening and expanding the areas of tension like a soothing balm.

7. If it feels safe and appropriate, you can give voice to the emotions that arise through words, sounds, or movements. You might also explore symbolic gestures or postures that embody the essence of the experience.

8. Trust that by allowing these authentic expressions to move through you, you are fostering greater somatic coherence. Over time, you may notice the physiological patterns of tension releasing and integrating as the associated emotions are processed and digested.

9. Remember to go slowly and attune to your body's needs throughout the practice. If you feel overwhelmed or disconnected at any point, take a pause and resource yourself with grounding breaths, self-soothing touch, or a mental image of a safe, peaceful place.

10. As you complete the exercise, take a few moments to rest in the afterglow of this self-attunement. Notice any shifts in your embodied experience and any sense of greater alignment between your physical, emotional, and mental states.

Closing

As you finish this practice, please take a moment to appreciate your body's innate wisdom and its capacity for integration and healing. Honor the courage it takes to face and express your authentic experiences and to bring your whole self into greater alignment. Consider incorporating this type of somatic coherence exercise into your regular self-care routine to deepen your mind-body connection and build emotional resilience. Remember, each moment of attunement to your embodied experience is an opportunity to foster greater wholeness, vitality, and ease. Trust in the transformative power of your presence and the innate intelligence of your soma.

EXERCISE: CREATING YOUR RESOURCE COLLAGE

This practice invites you to explore your embodied resource states through the lens of creativity and visual expression. By crafting a collage that represents your somatic experiences of safety, strength, calm, and joy, you can anchor these positive states in a tangible, accessible way. Having a visual catalog of your resources can help you more easily access these internal experiences when needed. Approach this practice with a spirit of curiosity, playfulness, and self-compassion, trusting that your creative process will reveal meaningful insights and resources.

Guided Instructions

1. Begin by gathering your art supplies: a sheet of paper or poster board, a collection of magazines, colored pencils or markers, scissors, and glue. Choose materials that feel inspiring and inviting to work with.

2. Find a comfortable workspace where you can spread out your supplies and leave your collage-in-progress setup. Ensure that you have ample time and space to engage in this creative exploration.

3. Take a few grounding breaths, allowing your awareness to settle into the present moment. Notice the sensations of your breath moving in and out and the weight of your body contacting the surface beneath you.

4. Now, guide your attention through a gentle body scan, starting at the crown of your head and moving down to the soles of your feet. As you scan each area, notice any positive somatic experiences that arise, such as a sense of warmth, spaciousness, or vitality.

5. Choose one of these resourced states to work with first. Recreate the felt sense of this experience in your body as vividly as possible. Notice the physical sensations, emotions, and any associated images or memories.

6. With this embodied experience in mind, begin to explore your magazine collection for images, words, colors, and textures that capture the essence of this resource state. Trust your intuition and let yourself be drawn to the elements that resonate with your inner experience.

7. Using your scissors, cut out the chosen images and words and arrange them on your paper or poster board. Play with different compositions and layouts until you find an arrangement that feels satisfying and true to your somatic resource.

8. Glue your chosen elements onto the paper, creating a visual representation of your embodied experience. You might add additional details or embellishments with your colored pencils or markers to further personalize your collage.

9. Continue this process with other resource states that emerged during your body scan or that you have identified in previous somatic explorations. You can create a single, integrated collage that encompasses all your resources or make separate collages for each distinct experience.

10. Remember, your resource collage is a living, evolving creation. You can continue to add to it over time as new somatic resources emerge or as your relationship with your existing resources deepens and changes.

Closing

As you complete your resource collage, take a moment to step back and appreciate the visual tapestry of your embodied experiences. Notice any feelings of gratitude, wonder, or self-recognition that arise as you behold your creation. Consider displaying your collage in a prominent place as a daily reminder of the somatic resources that live within you. You might also use your collage as a focal point for meditation or self-reflection, allowing the images and sensations to guide you back to your inner wellsprings of resilience and ease. Trust that by engaging in this creative practice, you are strengthening your ability to access and integrate your embodied resources, supporting your ongoing journey of healing and growth.

13. BEFRIENDING YOUR SHAME

Shame is a universal human experience that we have all encountered in some form. It is the feeling of being fundamentally flawed, unworthy, or unlovable—a sense of inner deficiency that can be so visceral and all-consuming that it feels like it permeates every cell of our being. For many, shame is a hidden struggle, a silent wound carried beneath the surface, shaping thoughts, behaviors, and relationships in profound and often painful ways.

In embodied healing, we recognize shame as not just a cognitive or emotional experience but a deeply somatic one. It is a full-body phenomenon, a physiological stress response that can leave us feeling trapped, collapsed, and disconnected from our inner wisdom and resources. Yet, as painful as shame can be, it is also an invitation—a call to turn towards our wounded parts with curiosity, compassion, and care and to discover the hidden gifts and lessons they hold.

UNDERSTANDING THE SOMATIC EXPERIENCE OF SHAME

To befriend our shame, we must first develop a deeper understanding of how it lives in our bodies. Shame manifests in a wide range of physical sensations and postural patterns, such as heat or flushing in the face and chest, heaviness or contraction in the body, tightening in the throat and voice, hollowing in the belly, feeling small or invisible, and a desire to hide or escape from others' gaze.

These physical experiences are part of a complex physiological stress response triggered when we feel exposed, vulnerable, or deficient. When we experience shame, our nervous system goes on high alert, releasing stress hormones that prepare us for fight, flight, or freeze.

The shame response is a highly adaptive survival mechanism that has evolved to help us navigate the complexities of social belonging and hierarchy. In our ancestral past, being rejected or cast out from the group could mean certain death, so our bodies developed a finely tuned system for detecting and responding to signs of social threat or disapproval.

In this sense, shame is a natural and necessary part of our human experience, a way our bodies try to keep us safe, protect us from the pain of isolation, and help us maintain essential social bonds and connections. However, in our modern world, this shame response can often become overactive or distorted, hijacking our sense of self-worth and leaving us feeling chronically inadequate, unlovable, or alone.

WORKING WITH SHAME SOMATICALLY

One of the most powerful tools for working with shame is the practice of embodied self-compassion—turning towards our suffering with kindness, care, and understanding. When in the grip of shame, our first instinct is often to turn away from ourselves, numb out, dissociate, or distract from the pain and discomfort. However, doing so reinforces patterns of self-abandonment and self-neglect that keep us trapped in cycles of shame and suffering.

Instead, we can choose to meet our shame with curiosity and care, turning towards our wounded parts with gentle, loving attention. We can place a hand on our heart or belly, take slow, deep breaths, and silently offer ourselves the tender, compassionate presence we would offer a dear friend or small child who was hurting.

As we do this, we create a new relationship with our shame based on self-acceptance, self-love, and self-respect. We begin to see shame as a part of our human experience that deserves to be held with gentleness and care, developing a felt sense of inner safety and resilience.

Another key somatic practice for working with shame is resourcing—cultivating positive, nourishing experiences that help regulate our nervous system and build our capacity for resilience and self-regulation. By intentionally cultivating experiences of safety, connection, and ease in our bodies, we counterbalance the effects of shame and trauma and build a foundation of a felt sense of security and groundedness.

Ultimately, befriending our shame is a journey of radical self-acceptance and self-love, learning to embrace all parts of ourselves, even those that feel most unworthy or unlovable. It is a journey of discovering the deep well of compassion, wisdom, and resilience within us and learning to draw upon that inner resource in times of struggle and pain.

As we re-negotiate our bodily relationship to shame, we begin to see that our worth and value as human beings are not contingent upon being perfect or always "getting it right." We develop a more flexible, adaptable sense of self that can weather life's storms with grace and resilience, experiencing a deeper sense of freedom, authenticity, and joy.

This journey of shame healing is not always easy or comfortable. It requires a willingness to turn towards our pain and discomfort, sit with the difficult sensations and emotions that arise, and meet them with patience, perseverance, and care. It requires a commitment to our growth and healing and trust in the innate wisdom and intelligence of our bodies.

But the rewards of this journey are immeasurable. As we learn to befriend our shame, we open up new possibilities for connection, creativity, and aliveness. We discover a deep sense of belonging to ourselves and the world around us, coming to know, in a visceral and embodied way, the truth of our inherent worth, beauty, and lovability.

EXERCISE: MEETING SHAME WITH COMPASSION

Shame is a visceral, full-body experience that is often driven by self-judgment and a sense of unworthiness. It can manifest as physical contraction, hiding, or a desire to disappear. This practice offers a gentle, compassionate way to develop a new internal relationship with your shame. By meeting the shamed parts of yourself with unconditional love and acceptance, you can begin to disarm shame's grip and open new possibilities for healing and self-expression. Remember, this is a gradual process that requires patience, courage, and a commitment to self-kindness.

Guided Instructions

1. Begin by finding a comfortable posture, either seated or lying down. Ensure that your body feels well-supported and at ease.

2. Take a few grounding breaths, allowing your awareness to settle into the present moment. Notice the sensations of your breath moving in and out and the weight of your body contacting the surface beneath you.

3. Now, guide your attention inward, tuning into any parts of yourself that feel burdened by shame. This might be a physical area, like your belly or your posture, or an aspect of your personality, like your sensitivity or your desires.

4. As you acknowledge these shameful parts, imagine meeting them with the consciousness of an unconditionally loving presence. This presence sees beyond the shame to the inherent worth and beauty of all that you are.

5. You can use nurturing self-touch or imagined holding to offer comfort to the shamed areas. Place a hand gently on your belly, your heart, or any other part that needs care. Imagine this touch as a transmission of deep acceptance and compassion.

6. Allow any emotions, images, or memories associated with shame to surface. Notice them with kind attention without trying to change or analyze them. Trust that by bringing them into the light of compassionate awareness, they can begin to transform and integrate.

7. Offer compassionate self-talk or reassurance to the shamed parts of yourself. You might say silently, "I see you. I understand why you feel this way. You are not alone. I am here with you. I love and accept you completely."

8. If you notice any resistance or difficulty meeting your shame with compassion, acknowledge that response with kindness. Remind yourself that it takes practice to shift entrenched patterns of self-judgment and that your intention to offer care is itself a profound act of healing.

9. Throughout the practice, remember to breathe deeply and go at a pace that feels safe and manageable. If you feel overwhelmed at any point, return to your grounded breaths, or take a break to reorient yourself to the present moment.

10. As you complete the practice, take a few moments to rest in the afterglow of this self-compassion. Notice any shifts in your embodied sense of shame and any feelings of softening, opening, or relief.

Closing

As you finish this practice, take a moment to honor your courage in turning towards your shame with caring attention. Recognize that by meeting this vulnerable part of yourself with compassion, you are planting seeds of self-love and transformation that will blossom over time. Consider integrating this practice into your daily self-care routine, even if only for a few breaths at a time. With regular tending, you can develop a stable, compassionate inner refuge that can hold and heal even the most painful experiences of shame. Trust in the power of your loving presence and your fundamental wholeness and worthiness beyond the temporary obscurations of self-judgment.

EXERCISE: RELEASING SHAME THROUGH MOVEMENT

Shame is an intense emotional experience that often gets bound up and stuck in the body as muscular tension, contraction, or collapse. Over time, these shame-based holding patterns can become chronic, limiting our capacity for authentic self-expression and connection. This practice offers an embodied, expressive way to release the pent-up energy of shame through movement. By allowing your shameful impulses to be felt, moved, and completed, you can support the healthy processing and integration of this challenging emotion. Remember, this is a powerful practice that requires gentleness, patience, and a commitment to self-care.

Guided Instructions

1. Begin by finding an open, private space where you have room to move freely. This might be a cleared area in your home, a dance studio, or a secluded outdoor location. Ensure that you feel safe and comfortable in your chosen environment.

2. Take a few minutes to tune into your body, noticing any areas where you feel physical sensations of shame. This might be a sense of contraction in your belly, a heaviness in your chest, or a desire to make yourself small and hidden.

3. As you attune to these shameful sensations, allow small, organic movements to emerge from these areas. The movements might be subtle at first, like a slight rocking or pulsing. Trust the wisdom of your body and let the shame impulses guide your expression.

4. Gradually give the movements permission to grow and evolve. You might find yourself shifting between postures of collapse and expansion, hiding, and revealing, tension and release. Allow the full range of your shameful experience to be expressed through your body.

5. Use your breath to fuel and support movements. Exhale fully, letting go of any held tension or stagnation. Inhale deeply, drawing in fresh energy and spaciousness. You might find yourself sighing, groaning, or even yelling as you move.

6. Explore different rhythms and qualities in your movements. You might move slowly and tentatively at times and then erupt into fast, chaotic motion. Play with levels, moving close to the ground or reaching up high. Allow yourself to travel through space, taking up more room as it feels authentic.

7. Throughout the practice, remember to stay present and attuned to your body's needs. If you feel overwhelmed or disconnected at any point, pause, and take a few grounding breaths. You can also place a hand on your heart or belly to reestablish a sense of self-contact and support.

8. As the movements begin to naturally settle and complete, take a few minutes to rest in stillness. Notice any shifts in your embodied experience of shame and any sensations of release, relief, or integration.

Closing

As you complete this practice, take a moment to acknowledge your courage in allowing your shame to be fully felt and moved. Recognize that by giving this emotion a safe, embodied outlet, you are supporting your innate capacity for healing and wholeness. Consider integrating this type of expressive movement practice into your regular self-care routine to prevent the build-up of stagnant emotional energy and maintain a sense of vitality and flow. Remember, your shame is not a static or fixed experience but rather a moving, changing energy that can be transformed through compassionate attention and authentic expression. Trust in the wisdom of your body to guide you toward greater freedom, self-acceptance, and ease.

EXERCISE: RECONNECTING WITH YOUR INNOCENCE

Beneath the layers of life experiences, conditioning, and self-protection, we all have an essential, innocent nature. This is the part of us that is open, curious, trusting, and spontaneously expressive. Over time, as we navigate the challenges and disappointments of life, this innocent essence can get covered over, leading to feelings of disconnection, heaviness, or guardedness. This practice offers a gentle way to peel back the layers and reconnect with the unburdened, childlike state that still lives within you. By reclaiming your innocence, you can invite more freedom, spontaneity, and joy into your embodied experience.

Guided Instructions

1. Begin by finding a comfortable posture, either seated or lying down. Ensure that your body feels well-supported and at ease.

2. Take a few full, cleansing breaths, allowing your awareness to turn inward. With each exhalation, imagine releasing any tensions, worries, or heaviness that you may be carrying.

3. Now, gently guide your awareness back in time to memories or sensations from your early childhood. You might recall specific moments of wonder, play, or connection. Tune into the general feeling of your younger self.

4. As you connect with these earlier states, invite the embodied experience of innocence to arise. This might feel like a softening in your face and belly, an openness in your chest, or a lightness in your limbs.

5. You can support this process with affirmations, either silently or aloud. Repeat phrases like, "I am innocent," "I am enough, just as I am," or "I am open to the wonder of life." Let these words resonate through your body, affirming your essential wholeness.

6. Consciously allow your body to settle into the spaciousness of this innocent state. You might imagine your breath moving into any areas of tightness or contraction, gently expanding them with each inhalation.

7. If you notice any resistance or difficulty connected with your innocence, follow those experiences with compassion. Acknowledge the ways that life may have challenged your trust or openness without judgment. Remind yourself that your innocence is an intrinsic part of you, even if it's been temporarily obscured.

8. Throughout the practice, focus on breathing fully and deeply. If your mind wanders or gets caught up in analysis, gently return your attention to the sensations of your breath and body.

9. As you feel ready to close the practice, take a few moments to rest in the afterglow of this innocent reconnection. Notice any shifts in your embodied state and any sensations of ease, openness, or curiosity.

Closing

As you complete this practice, please take a moment to honor your essential innocence and the courage it takes to reconnect with this tender part of yourself. Recognize that by nurturing your innocent nature, you are cultivating a sense of resilience, adaptability, and joy that can support you in navigating life's ups and downs. Consider integrating this type of self-connection into your daily routine, even if just for a few breaths at a time. With regular practice, you can strengthen your ability to access the unburdened, openhearted state that is your birthright. Trust in the power of your innocence to guide you towards greater aliveness, authenticity, and connection - with yourself, others, and the world around you.

EXERCISE: PROGRESSIVE MUSCLE RELAXATION FOR SHAME RELEASE

Progressive Muscle Relaxation (PMR) for Shame Release is an exercise that combines the technique of PMR with mindful awareness and self-compassion to help you release and transform experiences of shame held in the body. Shame is a deeply embodied emotion that can manifest as chronic tension, constriction, or collapse in different areas of the body. By systematically tensing and relaxing muscle groups while bringing compassionate attention to the physical sensations of shame, you can start to unwind patterns of holding and bracing, and cultivate a greater sense of safety, acceptance, and ease in your body. This practice invites you to approach your embodied experience of shame with curiosity, gentleness, and a willingness to let go, and to explore the possibility of greater freedom and self-acceptance through the process of mindful release.

Steps

1. Find a quiet, private space where you can lie down comfortably without disturbance. Make sure you have enough room to stretch out and move freely, and that the temperature and lighting feel supportive for relaxation.

2. Lie down on your back, with your arms by your sides and your legs extended. Take a few deep breaths, allowing your body to settle and your mind to become present. Notice the sensations of your body making contact with the surface beneath you, and the gentle rise and fall of your belly with each inhale and exhale.

3. Bring to mind an experience of shame that you feel ready to work with, one that you can sense being held in your body in some way. This may be a current or past situation where you felt exposed, inadequate, or fundamentally flawed in some way.

4. As you recall this experience, scan your body and notice where you feel the shame most strongly. This may be a sense of tightness in your chest, a knot in your stomach, a heaviness in your throat, or a general sense of contraction or collapse throughout your body. Acknowledge these sensations with kindness and acceptance, knowing that they are a natural part of the shame experience.

5. Starting with your feet and toes, gently tense the muscles in this area, scrunching your toes and contracting the soles of your feet. As you do this, imagine breathing into any sense of shame or holding in this part of your body, acknowledging its presence with compassion.

6. Hold the tension for a few seconds, and then release, allowing your feet and toes to relax completely. As you exhale, imagine any shame or constriction being released from this area, flowing out of your body and into the earth below.

7. Move your attention up to your calves and shins, and repeat the process of tensing and relaxing, breathing into any sense of shame or holding, and releasing it with each exhalation. Continue this process through each muscle group in your body, moving from your legs to your hips and buttocks, your belly and chest, your arms and hands, your shoulders and neck, and finally your face and head.

8. As you tense and release each muscle group, stay attuned to any emotions, memories, or sensations that arise in connection with your experience of shame. Meet these experiences with gentleness and understanding, acknowledging their presence without getting lost in their story or meaning.

9. If at any point you feel overwhelmed or disconnected, take a few deep breaths and bring your attention back to the sensations of tensing and relaxing in your body. Remember that you are not your shame, and that this practice is an opportunity to release and transform painful emotions, not to reinforce or identify with them.

10. Once you have moved through your whole body, take a few deep breaths and notice the overall sense of relaxation and openness in your physical being. Notice any shifts in your experience of shame, and any sense of greater ease, acceptance, or compassion that may have emerged through this practice.

11. When you feel ready, gently wiggle your fingers and toes, and slowly roll to one side, using your arms to press yourself up to a seated position. Take a few moments to reorient to your surroundings, and to appreciate your own courage and willingness to engage in this transformative practice.

Conclusion

By combining the deep relaxation of PMR with mindful awareness and self-compassion, this practice can help you release patterns of chronic tension and holding, and develop a more accepting and nurturing relationship with your body and your emotional life.

Regular practice of PMR for Shame Release can support you in developing greater resilience and flexibility in the face of difficult emotions, and in cultivating a sense of safety and belonging in your own skin. While the process of releasing shame from the body is not always easy or comfortable, it is a journey of profound healing and self-discovery, one that can lead to greater wholeness, authenticity, and joy in all areas of life.

EXERCISE: BREATH-GUIDED SHAME COMPASSION PRACTICE

Breath-Guided Shame Compassion Practice is an exercise that combines the power of diaphragmatic breathing with the cultivation of self-compassion to help you transform and heal experiences of shame. Shame is a deeply painful emotion that can leave us feeling isolated, unworthy, and disconnected from our own humanity and the humanity of others. By bringing the soothing rhythm of the breath together with the warmth and understanding of self-compassion, you can start to soften the grip of shame and reconnect with your innate goodness and lovability. This practice invites you to use your breath as an anchor of compassionate presence, and to offer yourself the kindness, care, and acceptance needed to embrace and transform the parts of yourself that have been hidden or rejected due to shame.

Steps

1. Find a quiet, private space where you can sit comfortably without disturbance. Choose a position that allows your spine to be upright but not rigid, and your body to feel both alert and relaxed.

2. Close your eyes and take a few deep breaths, allowing your body to settle and your mind to become present. Notice the sensations of your breath moving in and out of your body, and the gentle rise and fall of your belly with each inhale and exhale.

3. Bring to mind an experience of shame that you feel ready to explore with compassion and

understanding. This may be a current or past situation where you have felt inadequate, unworthy, or fundamentally flawed in some way.

4. As you recall this experience, notice any physical sensations, emotions, or thoughts that arise in response. You may feel a tightness in your chest, a sinking feeling in your stomach, or a sense of heat or flushing in your face. Allow yourself to be present with these experiences, without trying to change or judge them.

5. Now, begin to deepen and slow your breath, focusing on breathing into your belly and lower ribcage. Imagine each inhalation gently expanding and softening any areas of tension or constriction, and each exhalation releasing and letting go of any painful emotions or self-judgments.

6. As you continue to breathe deeply and slowly, silently offer yourself words of compassion and understanding on each inhalation. You may say to yourself, "I see you," "I'm here with you," or "You are not alone." Let these words be a soothing balm for the painful emotions of shame.

7. On each exhalation, silently offer yourself words of forgiveness and acceptance. You may say to yourself, "I forgive you," "You are human," or "You are loved." Let these words be a gentle reminder of your own inherent worth and goodness, despite any mistakes or shortcomings.

8. Continue to breathe in self-compassion and breathe out self-forgiveness for several minutes, allowing the rhythm of your breath to anchor and deepen your practice. If you notice your mind wandering or getting caught up in shame-based thoughts, gently redirect your attention back to your breath and your chosen phrases of compassion.

9. As you feel ready, begin to expand your compassion to include others who may be experiencing shame in this moment. With each inhalation, silently offer them the same words of understanding and care that you have offered yourself. With each exhalation, silently offer them the same words of forgiveness and acceptance.

10. Take a few more deep breaths, and then gently release your focus on the shame experience and your compassionate phrases. Notice any shifts in your body, heart, or mind that may have occurred through this practice, and take a moment to appreciate your own courage and willingness to meet shame with compassion.

11. When you feel ready, slowly open your eyes and take a few moments to reorient to your surroundings. You may want to place a hand on your heart or belly as a gesture of self-care and support, and to carry the energy of compassion with you into the rest of your day.

Conclusion

Breath-Guided Shame Compassion Practice was included in this book because it offers a powerful way to alchemize the painful experience of shame through the transformative power of self-compassion. By anchoring our compassion practice in the soothing rhythm of the breath, we can cultivate a sense of safety, presence, and emotional regulation in the face of even our most difficult and painful feelings.

Regular practice of Breath-Guided Shame Compassion can help us develop the capacity to meet shame with kindness and understanding, rather than judgment or avoidance. It can support us in reconnecting with our own basic goodness and humanity, and in extending that recognition to others who may be struggling with similar feelings of inadequacy or unworthiness.

While the journey of shame healing is not always easy, it is a path of profound transformation and liberation. By learning to breathe compassion into the constricted places of our hearts and minds, we can gradually dissolve the barriers of shame that keep us isolated and disconnected, and open to a greater sense of belonging, wholeness, and love. May this practice be a nourishing resource on your own journey of healing and awakening.

EXERCISE: HEART-CENTERED SHAME RELEASE VISUALIZATION

Heart-Centered Shame Release Visualization is an exercise that combines the power of guided imagery with the wisdom and compassion of the heart to help you release and transform painful experiences of shame. Shame is a deeply rooted emotion that can leave us feeling trapped, unlovable, and disconnected from our own inner goodness and the goodness of others. By engaging the power of visualization and connecting with the intelligence of the heart, you can start to dissolve the layers of shame that may be obscuring your true nature and potential. This practice invites you to access the healing energy of self-forgiveness and self-acceptance, and to use the power of your imagination to transform shame into a catalyst for growth, resilience, and positive change.

Steps

1. Begin by finding a quiet, comfortable space where you can sit or lie down without disturbance. If you have an HRVB device, attach it according to the manufacturer's instructions and start the recording process.

2. Close your eyes and take a few deep breaths, allowing your body to settle and your mind to become present. Bring your attention to the sensation of your breath moving in and out, and the gentle rise and fall of your chest and belly.

3. Now, bring to mind an experience or pattern of shame that you feel ready to release and transform. This may be a specific situation where you felt exposed, judged, or fundamentally flawed, or a more general sense of unworthiness or inadequacy.

4. As you connect with this experience of shame, notice where you feel it most strongly in your body. You may sense a heaviness in your chest, a knot in your stomach, or a tightness in your throat. Allow yourself to be present with these sensations, without trying to change or judge them.

5. Now, imagine that you can see or sense your heart at the center of your chest. Picture it as a warm, glowing source of light and compassion, radiating unconditional love and acceptance to all parts of

your being.

6. As you focus on your heart, silently ask it for guidance and support in releasing and transforming the shame you are holding. Trust that your heart has the wisdom and compassion needed to help you heal and grow.

7. Now, imagine that with each inhalation, you are drawing the energy of shame from all parts of your body and mind into your heart center. Picture the shame as a dark, heavy substance that has been weighing you down and obscuring your true nature.

8. As you exhale, imagine that the warm, glowing light of your heart is completely dissolving and transmuting the shame, releasing it from your being and replacing it with pure, radiant love and acceptance. Picture the shame being transformed into light, and feel the sense of spaciousness and freedom that comes with letting it go.

9. Continue this visualization process for several minutes, using your breath to draw the shame into your heart and your heart's light to dissolve and transform it. If your mind wanders or you get caught up in shame-based thoughts, gently redirect your attention back to your heart and the power of its healing light.

10. As you feel ready, imagine that your entire being is now filled with the warm, glowing energy of self-compassion and self-acceptance. Picture yourself standing tall and radiant, free from the burden of shame and connected to your own innate goodness and worth.

11. Take a few deep breaths, and then gently release the visualization, allowing your heart and your whole being to integrate the healing energy you have generated.

12. When you feel ready, slowly open your eyes and take a few moments to reorient to your surroundings. If you are using an HRVB device, stop the recording and take note of any changes in your heart rate variability or emotional state.

13. Take a moment to appreciate yourself for the courage and compassion you have shown in engaging with this practice. Know that the more you work with shame in this way, the more you will be able to access the healing power of your own heart and release the limiting beliefs and emotions that may be holding you back.

Conclusion

By harnessing the power of guided imagery and connecting with the wisdom of the heart, we can start to dismantle the walls of shame that keep us isolated and disconnected, and access the innate resilience and radiance of our true nature.

Regular practice of Heart-Centered Shame Release Visualization can help us develop a more compassionate and accepting relationship with ourselves, and cultivate the self-forgiveness and self-love needed to heal old wounds and step into our fullest potential. It can support us in reconnecting with the goodness and worthiness at the core of our being.

14. NAVIGATING AROUSAL AND OVERWHELM

In the journey of embodied healing, cultivating the ability to navigate the complex terrain of our nervous system arousal is crucial. As human beings, we are designed to function optimally within a "window of tolerance"—a range of activation where we feel relatively stable, grounded, and engaged with the world around us. However, when we experience stress, trauma, or overwhelm, this delicate balance can be disrupted, leaving us feeling either hyper-aroused and anxious or hypo-aroused and shut down.

These states of dysregulation can become a chronic backdrop to our daily lives, leaving us feeling exhausted, disconnected, and out of control. We may find ourselves caught in cycles of reactivity and collapse, unable to access our inner resources and wisdom when we need them most. Yet, as challenging as these experiences can be, they also offer us a profound opportunity for growth, healing, and transformation.

STRATEGIES FOR STAYING WITHIN YOUR WINDOW OF TOLERANCE

The concept of the "window of tolerance" is at the heart of nervous system regulation. When we are within our window of tolerance, we have access to our full range of cognitive, emotional, and social capacities, feeling open, curious, and connected, able to navigate life's ups and downs with relative ease.

However, when we experience stress or trauma, our nervous system can quickly become dysregulated, pushing us outside of our window of tolerance into states of hyper-arousal (agitated, anxious, on edge) or hypo-arousal (numb, disconnected, shut down).

The first step in navigating these states is developing a deeper awareness of our somatic experience. By tuning into the subtle cues and signals of our body, we can start to recognize when we are moving out of our window of tolerance and take steps to regulate and stabilize our nervous system.

One powerful technique is the practice of "grounding"—intentionally connecting with the physical sensations of the present moment to help anchor and stabilize our nervous system. This might involve feeling the support of the ground beneath your feet, noticing the texture and temperature of the air on your skin, paying attention to the gentle rise and fall of your breath, or holding a comforting object.

Another key strategy for navigating arousal is the practice of "titration"—gently and gradually working with small amounts of activation or intensity rather than trying to push through or override our nervous system's natural responses. This involves taking regular breaks during stressful situations, practicing self-care activities that soothe and regulate our nervous system, seeking out supportive relationships and environments, and engaging in activities that bring us joy and a sense of accomplishment.

As we practice titration, we learn to trust and respect the natural wisdom of our nervous system and work with our arousal in a way that feels sustainable and nourishing over the long term.

Navigating the complex terrain of our nervous system is not always straightforward. There may be times when, despite our best efforts, we find ourselves stuck in cycles of hyper- or hypo-arousal. In these moments, reaching out for support from a skilled therapist, counselor, or other healing professional can be incredibly helpful.

With the help of a supportive and knowledgeable guide, we can create a safe and nurturing container for our healing work, allowing us to gently explore and release the underlying patterns of trauma and overwhelm that may be fueling our dysregulation. We can develop a greater sense of trust and attunement with our body's signals and needs and cultivate the inner resources and resilience that will support us on our journey of growth and transformation.

EXERCISE: GROUNDING AND CENTERING

Grounding refers to the experience of feeling rooted, stable, and centered in your body. When you are grounded, you have a sense of being fully present and anchored in the here and now. This practice offers a way to cultivate embodied presence and inner stabilization, which can be particularly helpful during times of stress, overwhelm, or disconnection. By learning to ground and center yourself, you can access greater resilience, clarity, and self-regulation in the face of life's challenges.

Guided Instructions

1. Begin by finding a comfortable upright posture, either seated or standing. If seated, ensure that your feet are flat on the floor and your spine is self-supporting. If standing, have your feet about hip-width apart and your knees slightly soft.

2. Take a few deep, slow breaths into your belly, allowing your awareness to settle fully into your body. Notice the sensations of your breath moving in and out, as well as any areas of tightness or holding.

3. Begin to feel the connection between your body and the earth beneath you. If seated, feel your sit bones and feet contacting the ground. If standing, feel the weight of your body transferring down through your legs and feet into the floor.

4. Imagine that you have roots extending down from the base of your body, like a tree. With each exhalation, feel these roots sinking deeper into the earth, anchoring you in a sense of stability and support.

5. Gently engage your core muscles by drawing your lower abdomen slightly inward. This action helps to create a sense of central alignment and inner strength. Maintain this engagement with a sense of ease, without gripping or tension.

6. Align your head so that it sits smoothly over your erect spine as if your vertebrae were a series of stacked bones. Imagine a sense of length and spaciousness in your neck and throughout your spine.

7. You can further enhance your sense of grounding by visualizing a cord of energy descending from the base of your spine deep into the earth. This cord acts as a conduit, allowing any excess tension, anxiety, or scattered thoughts to drain out of your body and into the ground.

8. Throughout the practice, remember to keep breathing fully and naturally. If you notice any areas of unnecessary tension, use your exhale to release and soften those spots.

9. Take a few moments to rest in this state of grounded presence. Notice how it feels to be centered and stable in your body while still maintaining a sense of alertness and readiness.

Closing

As you complete this practice, take a moment to appreciate your body's innate capacity for grounding and self-regulation. Notice any shifts in your sense of embodied presence, stability, or clarity. Consider integrating this centering practice into your daily routine, perhaps as a way to start your day or as a tool to use during moments of transition or intensity. With regular practice, you can cultivate a more consistent sense of groundedness that can support you in navigating life's ups and downs with greater ease and resilience. Remember, your body is always here as a source of wisdom, strength, and support - all you need to do is tune in and connect with its stabilizing presence.

EXERCISE: TITRATION AND PENDULATION

Titration and pendulation are two key principles in somatic experiencing, a body-based approach to healing trauma and stress. Titration involves gradually exposing oneself to small, manageable doses of intense sensations or emotions rather than becoming overwhelmed by them all at once. Pendulation refers to the natural oscillation between activation and settling that occurs in the body when processing difficult experiences. By learning to titrate and pendulate, you can expand your "window of tolerance" for challenging states in a safe, controlled way, promoting greater resilience and emotional regulation.

Guided Instructions

1. Begin by finding a safe, comfortable space where you can explore this practice without interruption. Ensure that you have any resources or support you might need, such as a cozy blanket, a journal, or a grounding object.

2. Take a few slow, deep breaths, allowing your body to settle into a state of centered presence. Notice

the sensations of your breath moving in and out, as well as any areas of tension or relaxation.

3. Gently guide your awareness inward and select an activating issue or experience that you'd like to work with. This might be a current stressor, a past trauma, or a difficult emotion. Choose something that feels manageable and not too overwhelming.

4. Allow yourself to connect with the emotional and somatic experience of this issue. Notice any sensations, images, or thoughts that arise without becoming absorbed in them. Imagine that you are titrating or letting in just a small amount of the activation at a time.

5. As you feel the intensity begin to build, take a few deep breaths, and focus on any sensations of groundedness or support in your body. You might feel your feet on the floor, your sit bones on the chair, or your back against a wall. These are your resources or anchors of stability.

6. Allow the wave of activation to peak and then naturally subside, like a pendulum swinging back towards the center. As the intensity dissipates, keep breathing fully and noticing any sensations of settling or release in your body.

7. When you feel relatively stable and resourced again, you can choose to titrate a bit more intensity, building on your previous capacity. Remember to go slowly and honor your body's limits. If at any point you feel overwhelmed, return to your resources, and allow the activation to pendulate back down.

8. You can incorporate gentle movements or vocalizations to support the processing and release of the activated energy. You might shake, sway, or make sounds, staying attuned to what feels authentic and relieving for your body.

9. Continue this process of titrating and pendulating for as long as it feels appropriate. You may find that your capacity to hold intensity gradually expands, or you may reach a natural stopping point. Trust your body's wisdom, and don't push beyond your limits.

Closing

As you complete this practice, take a few moments to acknowledge your courage in working with challenging experiences in a mindful, titrated way. Notice any shifts in your capacity to hold and process intensity and any sensations of relief, spaciousness, or integration in your body. Remember that titration and pendulation are skills that develop with practice and that each session is an opportunity to build your resilience and expand your window of tolerance. Consider integrating this approach into your self-care routine, either on your own or with the support of a trained therapist. Trust in your body's innate wisdom and its capacity to find balance and healing when given the right conditions and care.

EXERCISE: SENSORY MODULATION TECHNIQUES

Sensory modulation refers to the capacity to regulate the nervous system's arousal levels in response to sensory input. By learning to skillfully use different sensory techniques, you can help your body and mind achieve an optimal "window of tolerance" - a state of calm-focused attunement. Some sensory inputs can be soothing and grounding when you feel hyper-aroused or anxious, while others can be stimulating and energizing when you feel hypo-aroused or lethargic. Experiment with these different techniques to discover what works best for your unique sensory system.

Guided Instructions

1. Begin by tuning into your current state of activation or depletion. Notice any sensations of restlessness, agitation, or anxiety that might indicate hyper-arousal. Or observe any feelings of fatigue, spaciness, or low motivation that could point to hypo-arousal.

2. If you're feeling hyper-aroused or overstimulated, try one or more of these calming techniques:

- Apply deep pressure to your body through self-massage, hugging, or wrapping yourself tightly in a blanket. The weight and compression can help you feel more grounded and contained.
- Engage in slow, rhythmic movements like rocking, swaying, or gentle stretching. These repetitive motions can be soothing to the nervous system and help discharge excess energy.
- Use your voice to hum, chant, or sing in a low, calming tone. The vibrations and resonance can promote a sense of internal stability and regulation.
- Focus on regulating your breath by slowing down the inhale and elongating the exhale. You can count your breaths or use phrases like "in" and "out" to help maintain a steady, grounding rhythm.

3. If you're feeling hypo-aroused or under-responsive, try one or more of these stimulating techniques:

- Engage in brisk, invigorating movements like jumping jacks, high knees, or shaking out your limbs. These exercises can boost your energy and alertness.
- Listen to upbeat, energizing music that makes you want to move and engage with your surroundings. The rhythm and tempo can help shift your nervous system into a more active state.
- Smell strong, stimulating scents like citrus, peppermint, or rosemary. These aromas can be awakening and help clear any mental fog or dullness.
- Eat or drink something with a crunchy, chewy, or sour texture, like a crisp apple, a piece of gum, or a tart beverage. The intense sensations can help stimulate your senses and boost your focus.

4. Remember that sensory modulation is a highly individual process, so what works for one person

may not work for another. Be open to experimenting with different techniques and pay attention to how your body and mind respond. Over time, you can develop a personalized "sensory diet" that helps you regulate your arousal levels throughout the day.

Closing

As you complete this practice, take a few moments to notice any shifts in your arousal levels or overall sense of regulation. Acknowledge the power of sensory input to influence your internal state and the wisdom of your body in knowing what it needs to find balance. Consider integrating regular "sensory check-ins" into your daily routine, taking brief pauses to assess your arousal, and responding with appropriate modulation techniques. Over time, you can build a more flexible, resilient nervous system that can adapt to a range of sensory experiences. Remember, your senses are always providing valuable information and opportunities for self-care - all you need to do is listen and respond with curiosity and compassion.

EXERCISE: RAIN (RECOGNIZE, ALLOW, INVESTIGATE, NURTURE)

RAIN is a powerful mindfulness tool for meeting difficult emotions with compassion and insight. It is an acronym that stands for Recognize, Allow, Investigate, and Nurture. This practice helps us to step out of reactivity and into a more spacious, compassionate relationship with our inner experiences.

By learning to RAIN, we can transform challenging emotions into opportunities for greater self-understanding, wisdom, and self-compassion. This practice cultivates emotional resilience and a deeper sense of inner freedom.

Remember, the goal is not to fix or change your emotions but to meet them with open, caring awareness. Trust that this process of mindful attention and self-compassion is deeply healing and transformative.

Guided Instructions

1. Recognize: Begin by recognizing that you are caught in a difficult emotional state. This might be anxiety, anger, sadness, shame, or any other challenging feeling. Pause and acknowledge what is happening, silently naming it to yourself. For example, "I'm noticing anxiety" or "There's a lot of sadness present."

2. Allow: The next step is to allow the emotion to be there, just as it is. This does not mean you like it or want it to continue. It means you are permitting it to exist without trying to push it away or control it. You might silently say to yourself, "It's okay to feel this," or "I can make space for this emotion."

3. Investigate: Now, begin to investigate the emotion with a spirit of gentle curiosity. You might ask yourself, "Where do I feel this in my body? What are the sensations?" Notice if there are any thoughts or beliefs associated with the emotion, like "I can't handle this" or "This will never end." See if you can identify any unmet needs or desires beneath the emotion, like a longing for safety, connection, or understanding.

4. Nurture: Finally, offer yourself some nurturing, compassionate care. Place a hand on your heart or another soothing place, and silently offer yourself kind words or phrases. For example, "I'm here for you" or "You're not alone in this." You might also ask yourself, "What do I need right now to feel supported?" It could be a message of understanding, a comforting touch, or an action step for self-care.

5. As you complete the RAIN process, take a few deep breaths, and notice any shifts in your emotional state or overall sense of well-being. Remember that it is normal for difficult emotions to still be present. The goal is not to eliminate them but to relate to them with more mindfulness and compassion.

Tips and Variations

- You can practice RAIN as a seated meditation, or you can use it on the spot whenever difficult emotions arise. With practice, it can become a habitual way of relating to your inner world.
- If you are newer to mindfulness, you might find it helpful to spend more time on the Recognize and Allow steps, really anchoring your attention in the present-moment experience of the emotion. As you become more practiced, you can deepen the Investigation and Nurture steps.
- Remember that self-compassion is a key part of RAIN. If you find yourself slipping into self-judgment or criticism during the process, see if you can gently redirect your attention back to self-kindness and care.
- You can also practice RAIN for positive emotions to deepen your capacity for savoring and appreciating the good in life. The same steps apply: Recognize the positive emotion, allow it to be there, investigate how it feels in the body and mind, and Nurture it with gratitude and care.

Closing

RAIN is a transformative practice for meeting life's challenges with greater presence, wisdom, and compassion. By learning to Recognize, Allow, Investigate, and Nurture our difficult emotions, we can tap into our innate capacity for resilience and healing.

Remember, like any mindfulness practice, RAIN is most transformative when practiced regularly. Consider setting an intention to RAIN daily or whenever you notice yourself caught in emotional reactivity.

EXERCISE: MINDFUL AROUSAL AWARENESS PRACTICE

Mindful Arousal Awareness Practice is an exercise that combines mindfulness techniques from Mindfulness-Based Stress Reduction (MBSR) and Mindfulness-Based Cognitive Therapy (MBCT) with the cultivation of awareness around states of physiological and emotional arousal. Arousal is a natural and necessary part of our human experience, helping us to mobilize energy and attention in response to stress, excitement, or other stimuli. However, when arousal becomes chronic or overwhelming, it can lead to feelings of anxiety, reactivity, or burnout. By bringing mindful awareness to our arousal states, we can start to develop greater self-regulation, resilience, and choice in how we respond to the ups and downs of life. This practice invites you to approach your arousal with curiosity, acceptance, and self-compassion, and to explore the possibility of finding greater balance and ease within the full spectrum of your experience.

Steps

1. Find a quiet, comfortable space where you can sit or lie down without disturbance. Choose a position that allows your body to be relaxed yet alert, and your mind to be present and awake.

2. Close your eyes and take a few deep breaths, allowing your body to settle and your mind to become present. Notice the sensations of your breath moving in and out, and the gentle rise and fall of your chest and belly.

3. Now, bring your attention to your body and mind, and notice any signs of arousal or activation that may be present. This could include physical sensations like a racing heart, tense muscles, or shallow breathing, as well as emotional or mental experiences like agitation, excitement, or scattered thoughts.

4. As you notice these signs of arousal, see if you can bring a sense of gentle curiosity and openness to your experience. Rather than trying to change or judge what you are feeling, simply allow it to be present, and observe it with a kind and accepting attention.

5. Now, choose one physical sensation of arousal to focus on, such as a tight chest, clenched jaw, or restless legs. Bring your full attention to this sensation, and see if you can explore it with all of your senses. What does it feel like? Is it sharp or dull, hot or cold, pulsing or still? Does it have a color, shape, or texture?

6. As you continue to explore this sensation, notice if there are any emotions or thoughts that arise in connection with it. Is there a sense of fear, excitement, or frustration? Are there any stories or judgments that your mind is telling about the arousal? Again, see if you can observe these experiences with kindness and acceptance, without getting caught up in their content.

7. Now, see if you can bring a sense of gentle compassion and care to the part of your body that is holding the arousal. You might imagine breathing into the sensation, or offering it a soothing touch or word of comfort. Let your attention be like a loving presence, holding the arousal with tenderness and understanding.

8. As you continue to bring mindful awareness and compassion to your arousal, notice if there are any shifts or changes in your experience. Does the sensation intensify, soften, or move to a different part of your body? Do any new emotions or insights arise? Allow yourself to be surprised and curious about the unfolding of your experience.

9. If at any point you feel overwhelmed or disconnected, take a few deep breaths and bring your attention back to the sensations of your breath and body. Remember that you are not trying to change or fix your arousal, but simply to be present with it in a kind and accepting way.

10. When you feel ready, gently release your focus on the specific sensation of arousal, and bring your attention back to your body and breath as a whole. Take a few deep breaths, and notice any changes in your overall sense of arousal and presence.

11. As you prepare to end the practice, take a moment to appreciate yourself for the curiosity and compassion you have brought to your experience. Remember that mindful awareness is a skill that grows with practice, and that each moment of presence is a gift to yourself and others.

12. When you feel ready, slowly open your eyes and take a few moments to reorient to your surroundings. Notice any shifts in your energy, perspective, or sense of well-being, and consider how you might carry the qualities of mindfulness and self-compassion into the rest of your day.

Conclusion

By learning to approach our arousal states with curiosity and acceptance, rather than judgment or reactivity, we can start to develop a more flexible and resilient nervous system, and a greater sense of choice and agency in how we respond to stress and stimulation.

Regular practice of Mindful Arousal Awareness can help us to break free from patterns of chronic tension, anxiety, or overwhelm, and to find a greater sense of balance and ease within the full spectrum of our human experience. It can support us in cultivating the mindfulness and self-compassion needed to navigate the challenges and opportunities of life with greater skill, creativity, and joy.

While the path of arousal awareness is not always easy or comfortable, it is a journey of profound growth and self-discovery. By learning to meet our arousal with the light of mindful attention and the warmth of self-compassion, we can gradually transform our relationship to stress and stimulation, and unlock the full potential of our mind, body, and spirit. May this practice be a valuable resource on your own journey of healing, growth, and awakening.

EXERCISE: PROGRESSIVE MUSCLE RELAXATION FOR AROUSAL REGULATION

Progressive Muscle Relaxation (PMR) for Arousal Regulation is an exercise that combines the technique of PMR with mindful awareness to help you manage and regulate states of heightened physiological and emotional arousal. When we experience stress, anxiety, or excitement, our bodies respond with increased muscle tension, heart rate, and breathing, which can lead to feelings of agitation, overwhelm, or exhaustion. By systematically tensing and relaxing different muscle groups while bringing mindful attention to the sensations of arousal in the body, you can start to develop greater control over your nervous system and cultivate a sense of calm and balance in the face of intense experiences. This practice invites you to use the tool of PMR to explore and regulate your arousal, and to find a greater sense of choice and resilience in how you respond to the demands of life.

Steps

1. Find a quiet, comfortable space where you can sit or lie down without disturbance. Choose a position that allows your body to be supported and relaxed, and your mind to be alert and present.

2. Close your eyes and take a few deep breaths, allowing your body to settle and your mind to become present. Notice the sensations of your breath moving in and out, and the gentle rise and fall of your chest and belly.

3. Now, bring your attention to your body and notice any signs of arousal or tension that may be present. This could include physical sensations like a racing heart, tense muscles, or shallow breathing, as well as emotional or mental experiences like agitation, restlessness, or anxiety.

4. Starting with your feet and toes, gently tense the muscles in this area, scrunching your toes and contracting the soles of your feet. As you tense these muscles, notice any sensations of arousal or activation that may be present, such as heat, tingling, or pulsing.

5. Hold the tension for a few seconds, and then release, allowing your feet and toes to relax completely. As you release the tension, notice any sensations of letting go or relaxation that may arise, such as heaviness, softness, or ease.

6. Take a few deep breaths, and then move your attention up to your calves and shins. Again, tense the muscles in this area, contracting your calves and lifting your feet off the ground. Notice any sensations of arousal or tension that may be present, and hold the tension for a few seconds.

7. Release the tension in your calves and shins, allowing them to relax completely. Notice any sensations of release or letting go that may arise, and take a few deep breaths

8. Continue this process of tensing and relaxing each muscle group, moving up through your body in the following sequence: thighs, hips and buttocks, stomach, chest, back, shoulders, arms and hands, neck, and face. For each area, tense the muscles while noticing any sensations of arousal or activation, hold the tension for a few seconds, and then release completely, noticing any sensations of relaxation

or ease.

9. As you move through the practice, pay attention to any patterns or insights that may emerge. Are there certain areas of your body that hold more tension or arousal than others? Are there any emotions or thoughts that arise in connection with the sensations of tension and release? Allow yourself to be curious and open to whatever arises, without judgment or expectation.

10. When you have completed the sequence, take a few deep breaths and notice the overall state of your body and mind. Notice any shifts in your level of arousal or tension, and any changes in your emotional or mental state.

11. As you prepare to end the practice, take a moment to appreciate yourself for the mindfulness and self-care you have brought to your experience. Remember that the skills of arousal regulation and self-compassion are ones that grow with practice, and that each moment of presence and acceptance is a gift to yourself and others.

12. When you feel ready, slowly open your eyes and take a few moments to reorient to your surroundings. Notice any changes in your energy, perspective, or sense of well-being, and consider how you might integrate the qualities of mindfulness and self-regulation into the rest of your day.

Conclusion

By combining the technique of PMR with mindful awareness, this practice can help us to develop greater control over our nervous system and cultivate a sense of calm and balance in the face of intense or challenging experiences.

Regular practice of PMR for Arousal Regulation can support us in breaking free from patterns of chronic tension, anxiety, or reactivity, and in finding a greater sense of choice and resilience in how we respond to stress and stimulation. It can help us to cultivate the mindfulness and self-compassion needed to navigate the full spectrum of our human experience with greater skill, wisdom, and ease.

EXERCISE: BREATH-GUIDED AROUSAL REGULATION PRACTICE

Breath-Guided Arousal Regulation Practice is an exercise that combines the power of conscious breathing with mindful awareness to help you regulate and balance states of physiological and emotional arousal. Our breath is a powerful tool for influencing our nervous system and shifting our state of activation, from the calming effects of deep, slow breathing to the energizing effects of rapid, shallow breathing. By bringing mindful attention to our breath and experimenting with different breathing patterns, we can learn to modulate our arousal levels and find a sense of balance and stability in the face of stress or intensity. This practice invites you to use your breath as an anchor of self-regulation and to explore the potential for greater choice and flexibility in how you respond to the changing conditions of your life.

Steps

1. Find a quiet, comfortable space where you can sit or lie down without disturbance. Choose a position that allows your body to be relaxed and supported, and your breath to flow freely and naturally.

2. Close your eyes and take a few deep breaths, allowing your body to settle and your mind to become present. Notice the sensations of your breath moving in and out, and the gentle rise and fall of your chest and belly.

3. Now, bring your attention to your overall state of arousal or activation. Notice any physical sensations, such as muscle tension, heart rate, or temperature changes, as well as any emotional or mental experiences, such as agitation, excitement, or anxiety. Simply observe these experiences with curiosity and openness, without trying to change them.

4. As you continue to breathe naturally, notice the quality and rhythm of your breath. Is it fast or slow, deep or shallow, smooth or choppy? See if you can observe your breath without judgment, as a reflection of your current state of arousal.

5. Now, begin to deepen and slow your breath, focusing on breathing into your belly and lower ribcage. Inhale through your nose for a count of four, pause briefly, and then exhale through your mouth for a count of six. Continue this pattern of breathing for a few minutes, noticing any changes in your physical, emotional, or mental state.

6. As you breathe deeply and slowly, imagine that each inhalation is bringing a sense of calm and stability into your body, and each exhalation is releasing any tension or agitation. You may want to visualize your breath as a soothing color or light, spreading throughout your body and bringing a sense of ease and balance.

7. If you find your mind wandering or your arousal level increasing, gently redirect your attention back to your breath and the sensations of breathing deeply and slowly. Remember that the goal is not to eliminate arousal, but to find a sense of choice and flexibility in how you relate to it.

8. After a few minutes of deep, slow breathing, experiment with changing your breathing pattern to one that is more energizing and activating. Inhale through your nose for a count of two, pause briefly, and then exhale through your mouth for a count of two. Continue this pattern of breathing for a few minutes, noticing any changes in your physical, emotional, or mental state.

9. As you breathe rapidly and shallowly, imagine that each inhalation is bringing a sense of energy and aliveness into your body, and each exhalation is releasing any stagnation or dullness. You may want to visualize your breath as a bright, vibrant color or light, awakening your senses and enlivening your mind.

10. After a few minutes of rapid, shallow breathing, return to your natural breathing pattern and take a few moments to observe your overall state of arousal. Notice any changes in your physical sensations, emotions, or thoughts, and any insights or reflections that may have arisen.

11. As you prepare to end the practice, take a few deep breaths and bring your attention back to your body as a whole. Notice any areas of ease or tension, and any overall sense of balance or imbalance.

12. When you feel ready, gently open your eyes and take a few moments to reorient to your surroundings. Consider how you might carry the skills and insights of this practice into your daily life, using your breath as a tool for self-regulation and resilience.

Conclusion

Breath-Guided Arousal Regulation Practice was included in this book because it offers a simple yet powerful way to harness the transformative potential of conscious breathing for self-regulation and resilience. By bringing mindful awareness to our breath and experimenting with different breathing patterns, we can learn to modulate our arousal levels and find a sense of choice and flexibility in how we respond to stress and intensity.

Regular practice of Breath-Guided Arousal Regulation can help us to cultivate a more balanced and responsive nervous system, and to develop the skills of self-awareness and self-care that are essential for navigating the challenges and opportunities of life. It can support us in finding a sense of calm and stability in the face of overwhelm, as well as a sense of energy and aliveness in the face of stagnation or depletion.

EXERCISE: HEART-CENTERED AROUSAL REGULATION VISUALIZATION

Heart-Centered Arousal Regulation Visualization is an exercise that combines the power of guided imagery with the wisdom and compassion of the heart to help you regulate and balance states of physiological and emotional arousal. When we are faced with stress, challenge, or intensity, our bodies and minds can become overwhelmed and reactive, leading to feelings of anxiety, depletion, or burnout. By connecting with the intelligence and resilience of the heart, we can learn to navigate these experiences with greater skill and ease, and to find a sense of calm and clarity amidst the storm. This practice invites you to use the power of visualization to access the healing energy of your heart, and to cultivate a sense of inner balance and coherence that can support you in the face of any arousal or activation.

Steps

1. Find a quiet, comfortable space where you can sit or lie down without disturbance. If you have a heart rate variability biofeedback (HRVB) device, attach it according to the manufacturer's instructions and start the recording process.

2. Close your eyes and take a few deep breaths, allowing your body to settle and your mind to become present. Bring your attention to the sensations of your breath moving in and out, and the gentle rise and fall of your chest and belly.

3. Now, bring your awareness to your heart center, in the middle of your chest. Imagine that you can see or sense your heart as a warm, glowing sphere of light, pulsing with the rhythm of your heartbeat.

4. As you focus on your heart, notice any sensations of ease or tension, openness or constriction. Simply observe these sensations with curiosity and acceptance, without trying to change them.

5. Now, imagine that with each inhalation, you are drawing in a sense of calm, balance, and coherence into your heart center. Visualize this energy as a cool, soothing color, like blue or green, filling your heart with a sense of peace and stability.

6. As you exhale, imagine that you are releasing any sensations of arousal, tension, or anxiety from your heart center. Visualize this energy as a warm, vibrant color, like red or orange, leaving your body and dissipating into the air around you.

7. Continue this visualization for several minutes, breathing in calm and balance, and breathing out arousal and tension. If your mind wanders or gets caught up in thoughts, gently redirect your attention back to your heart center and the flow of energy moving in and out.

8. As you settle into this practice, notice if there are any shifts or changes in your overall sense of arousal and activation. You may feel a sense of quieting in your mind, relaxation in your body, or expansion in your heart. Simply observe these changes with openness and curiosity.

9. If at any point you feel ungrounded or overwhelmed, imagine that you can send roots or cords of light from your heart center deep into the earth, anchoring you in a sense of stability and support. Feel the energy of the earth flowing up through these roots, bringing a sense of nourishment and resilience into your being.

10. When you feel ready, begin to expand your awareness to include your whole body and the space around you. Imagine that the energy of calm, balance, and coherence is now radiating out from your heart center, filling every cell and fiber of your being with a sense of ease and vitality.

11. Take a few deep breaths, and feel the integration of your mind, body, and heart in this state of centered, regulated arousal. Notice any insights, images, or sensations that may arise, and allow them to be present without attachment or interpretation.

12. As you prepare to end the practice, take a moment to acknowledge and appreciate your own capacity for self-regulation and resilience. Affirm your commitment to meeting the challenges and opportunities of life with an open, compassionate heart.

13. When you feel ready, gently open your eyes and take a few moments to reorient to your surroundings. If you are using an HRVB device, stop the recording and take note of any changes in your heart rate variability or emotional state.

Conclusion
Heart-Centered Arousal Regulation Visualization was included in this book because it offers a

powerful way to access the innate wisdom and resilience of the heart in the face of stress, intensity, or overwhelm. By using the tool of guided imagery to connect with the regulating and balancing energy of the heart, we can learn to navigate the ups and downs of arousal with greater skill and ease, and to find a sense of inner coherence and stability amidst the chaos of life.

Regular practice of Heart-Centered Arousal Regulation Visualization can help us to cultivate a more responsive and flexible nervous system, and to develop the capacity for self-regulation and self-care that is essential for thriving in a complex and changing world. It can support us in finding a sense of calm and clarity in the face of anxiety or overwhelm, as well as a sense of vitality and aliveness in the face of numbness or disconnection.

15. WORKING WITH DISSOCIATION

Dissociation is an innate human capacity to disconnect from our immediate sensory experience and retreat into an inner world of thoughts, fantasies, or numbness. This ability to "check out" from the here and now is a vital survival mechanism that allows us to endure overwhelming stress, pain, or trauma without becoming completely overwhelmed or shattered.

However, for many, dissociation can become more than a temporary coping strategy—it can become a chronic, pervasive way of being in the world, a habit of disconnection that leaves us feeling fragmented, unreal, and cut off from the vibrancy and aliveness of our own embodied experience. We may find ourselves drifting through life in a haze of detachment and unreality, struggling to fully engage with the people and activities that matter most to us.

In somatic healing, we understand that chronic dissociation is not a personal failure or weakness but a natural response to an overwhelming experience. This biological defense mechanism has become stuck in the "on" position. With patience, persistence, and skilled support, it is possible to gently coax our dissociated parts back into wholeness and re-weave the threads of our somatic experience into a cohesive and resilient tapestry.

UNDERSTANDING DISSOCIATION

Dissociation is a state of disconnection from our present-moment experience—a disruption in the normal integration of our thoughts, feelings, sensations, and behaviors. When we dissociate, we may feel spacey, foggy, or unreal, as if we are watching our lives unfold from a distance rather than fully participating in them. We may have gaps or blank spots in our memory or feel as if we are moving through the world on autopilot, disconnected from our sense of agency and choice.

The experience of dissociation exists on a continuum, ranging from mild, everyday experiences of spacing out or daydreaming to more severe and chronic forms of disconnection that can arise in the aftermath of trauma or abuse. While mild dissociation can be adaptive in certain situations, such as focusing intently on a task or using imagination to escape a boring or unpleasant situation, chronic dissociation can have profound impacts on our physical, emotional, and relational well-being.

At a physiological level, dissociation is mediated by the autonomic nervous system—the part of our nervous system that regulates our body's automatic survival responses, like fight, flight, or freeze. When we experience overwhelming stress or trauma, our autonomic nervous system can become dysregulated, triggering a cascade of physiological changes that prepare us to defend against threats, including a shift into a dissociative state.

RE-ASSOCIATING WITH YOUR SOMATIC EXPERIENCE

To work with chronic dissociation and invite our disconnected parts back into the fold of our embodied experience, one of the most important tools is the practice of grounding—intentionally connecting with the physical sensations and perceptions of the present moment to anchor ourselves in the here-and-now.

As we practice grounding ourselves in the present moment, we help re-orient our nervous system to the reality of our current experience rather than the remembered or imagined threats of the past or future. We begin to develop a felt sense of safety and stability in our bodies, a foundation of embodied presence that can support us as we explore the more vulnerable and dissociated parts of our experience.

Another key tool for working with dissociation is the practice of resourcing—intentionally connecting with positive, nourishing experiences that help to soothe and regulate our nervous system. As we cultivate a felt sense of safety and nourishment in our bodies, we begin to create a more hospitable environment for our dissociated parts to return to—a sense of welcome and inclusion that can help ease the protective defenses of our nervous system.

The journey of re-associating with our somatic experience is not always straightforward. Dissociation can be a deeply entrenched pattern, and it can take time, patience, and skilled support to begin to unwind its hold on our system.

One important skill in this process is the ability to titrate—to work with small, manageable doses of sensation and emotion rather than trying to force a full-scale confrontation with our dissociated experience all at once. As we practice titration, we begin to develop a greater capacity to tolerate and integrate the dissociated parts of our experience without becoming overwhelmed or re-traumatized in the process.

Another important aspect of working with dissociation is the cultivation of interoceptive awareness—the ability to notice and track our internal bodily sensations, like our heartbeat, breath, or the subtle cues of emotion and arousal in our system. As we practice tuning in to the subtle cues and signals of our body, we begin to re-establish a sense of connection and communication with our inner world, recognizing the early warning signs of dissociation and responding with grounding and resourcing practices that can help us stay present and embodied.

Over time, as we cultivate somatic awareness and attunement, our relationship to dissociation may shift and transform. We may start to experience dissociation as a fluid, dynamic process that we can navigate with skill and compassion, using our capacity for dissociation as a tool for self-regulation and creative exploration rather than a default mode of coping with stress and overwhelm.

EXERCISE: GROUNDING TECHNIQUES FOR DISSOCIATION

Dissociation refers to a sense of disconnection or detachment from one's immediate experience, often accompanied by feelings of numbness, spaciness, or unreality. While dissociation can serve as a protective response to overwhelming stress or trauma, it can also interfere with our ability to feel present and embody in the here and now. These grounding techniques are designed to help you re-associate and regain a sense of centered embodied awareness. Remember to approach this practice with gentleness and patience, honoring your system's natural defenses while gradually inviting more connection and groundedness.

Guided Instructions

1. Begin by noticing any signs that you may be dissociating, such as feeling spaced out, emotionally numb, or disconnected from your body. You might notice a sense of fogginess, a narrowing of your visual field, or a feeling of being outside yourself.

2. If you recognize that you are dissociating, take a gentle pause and acknowledge the experience without judgment. Remind yourself that dissociation is a natural response to stress or overwhelm and that you are taking steps to care for yourself at this moment.

3. To help re-engage your senses and bring your awareness back to the present, try one or more of these techniques:

- Look around your environment and describe what you see in detail. Name the colors, shapes, textures, and objects that catch your attention. This can help orient your visual perception to the here and now.
- Eat or drink something with a strong flavor, like a piece of lemon, a peppermint, or a sip of herbal tea. Notice the taste sensations on your tongue and the feeling of the food or liquid moving through your body.
- Squeeze or apply pressure to different parts of your body, like your hands, arms, or thighs. This can help activate your sense of touch and proprioception, reminding you of your physical boundaries and presence.
- Listen closely to the sounds in your environment, both near and far. See if you can distinguish between different layers of sound, like the hum of an appliance, the rustle of leaves, or the tone of someone's voice.

4. Find an object or surface in your surroundings that you can make solid, grounding contact with. This might be the floor beneath your feet, a piece of furniture, or a textured item like a smooth stone or a soft blanket. Focus on the sensations of connection and support.

5. Orient yourself to the current date, time, and location. You can say this information out loud or silently to yourself, anchoring your awareness in the present moment. For example, "It's Tuesday, April 5th at 3 pm. I'm in my living room at home."

6. Slowly and mindfully, begin to move your body in small ways, like wiggling your fingers and toes, rolling your shoulders, or gently rocking back and forth. Pay close attention to the sensations that arise as you move, letting your body's aliveness guide you back to a sense of embodied presence.

7. If you need additional support, you can access internal resource states by calling to mind imagery of people, places, or experiences that elicit feelings of safety, comfort, or ease. Let these positive associations help soothe and stabilize your nervous system.

Closing

As you complete this practice, take a few moments to acknowledge your system's innate wisdom and resilience in navigating challenges. Notice any shifts in your sense of presence, groundedness, or aliveness, celebrating every step towards re-association, no matter how small. Remember that building a sense of embodied safety and connection is a gradual, nonlinear process - one that requires ongoing patience, attunement, and self-compassion. Consider integrating these grounding techniques into your daily life, leaning on them whenever you need a gentle reminder of your body's inherent ability to heal, regulate, and come home to itself. Trust that with each practice, you are strengthening your capacity to remain anchored in the present, even amidst the waves of your inner experience.

EXERCISE: ORIENTING TO THE PRESENT MOMENT

This practice is designed to help anchor your awareness in the here and now, cultivating a sense of grounded presence and embodied connection. By intentionally orienting to the present moment, you can disembark from rumination about the past or worries about the future and instead attune to the felt experience of being alive right now. This skill is a valuable tool for self-regulation, as it can help disarm reactive patterns and promote a state of centered responsive awareness. With regular practice, orienting to the present moment can become a powerful habit for navigating life's challenges with greater ease and resilience.

Guided Instructions

1. Wherever you are, take a gentle pause from whatever you are doing or thinking about. If it is comfortable, close your eyes for a moment to help shift your attention inward.

2. Begin by feeling your body's connection to the ground or surface beneath you. If you are sitting, feel the weight of your body on the chair and your feet on the floor. If you are standing, feel the pressure of your feet against the earth. If you are lying down, feel the support of the surface below you.

3. Bring your awareness to the physical sensations of breathing. Notice the cool air entering your nostrils, the expansion of your chest and belly, and the warm air leaving your body. Allow your breath to find its natural rhythm, not forcing or controlling it in any way.

4. Now, open your eyes and use your senses to take in your present surroundings. Start by visually scanning the environment around you, noticing the colors, shapes, and textures that you see. Describe

these aloud to yourself in a factual, non-judgmental way, like "I see a green plant, a wooden table, a white wall."

5. Shift your attention to your sense of hearing and spend a few moments just listening to the sounds around you. You might notice the hum of appliances, the rustle of leaves outside, or the distant murmur of traffic. See if you can listen without labeling or interpreting the sounds, just letting them be as they are.

6. Notice any smells or aromas in your environment and feel the temperature and movement of the air on your skin. Is it cool or warm? Is there a breeze or a sense of stillness? Again, try to stay with the raw sensations without getting caught up in preferences or evaluations.

7. If you like, you can do a quick body scan to further arrive in your physical presence. Starting at your feet and moving up to your head, notice the sensations in each part of your body without trying to change anything. You might feel tingling, pulsing, pressure, warmth, or coolness. If you encounter any areas of tension or discomfort, acknowledge them with kindness and move on.

8. To deepen your sense of embodiment, you can do some light stretching or gentle movements, like rolling your shoulders, circling your wrists, or gently twisting from side to side. Keep your movements slow and mindful, staying connected to the sensations that arise.

9. Throughout the practice, keep returning to your breath as an anchor, noticing the constant flow of air in and out of your body. If your mind wanders into thoughts or judgments, gently guide it back to the simplicity of the present moment.

Closing

As you complete this practice, take a moment to appreciate your ability to anchor yourself in the present moment, no matter what may be happening in your inner or outer world. Notice any shifts in your state of being - perhaps you feel a little more grounded, clear, or connected to yourself and your surroundings. Remember that orienting to the present is a skill that grows stronger with repetition, so be patient and persistent in your practice. Consider setting aside a few minutes each day to pause and arrive in the here and now, using the simple tools of breath, sensation, and sensory awareness. Over time, you may find that this practice becomes a valuable resource for navigating the inevitable ups and downs of life with greater stability, ease, and grace.

EXERCISE: DEVELOPING A SOMATIC ANCHOR

A somatic anchor is a deliberately cultivated embodied resource state that you can access whenever you need to feel more grounded, calm, or centered. By intentionally evoking and encoding a felt sense of safety and ease, you create a portable tool for self-regulation and resilience. Having a reliable somatic anchor can be particularly helpful in moments of stress, overwhelm, or dysregulation, as it provides a visceral reminder of your innate capacity for stability and well-being. With practice, you can learn to drop into this anchored state with increasing ease and rapidity, enhancing your overall sense of emotional and physiological resilience.

Guided Instructions

1. Begin by finding a comfortable posture, either seated or lying down. Choose a position that allows you to feel both alert and relaxed, with your spine relatively straight but not rigid.

2. Take a few slow, deep breaths, allowing your awareness to turn inward. With each exhalation, feel your body settling more fully into the support beneath you, letting go of any unnecessary tension or holding.

3. Now, guide your attention through a gentle body scan, starting at the crown of your head and gradually moving down to the soles of your feet. As you scan each region, notice any physical sensations that are present without trying to change or judge them.

4. As you attune to your body, invite a sense of ease, stillness, and safety to arise. You might imagine a warm, soothing light permeating your entire being or a gentle wave of relaxation flowing through you. Allow yourself to marinate in this experience of embodied tranquility.

5. To enhance the feeling of anchoring, you can call to mind an image of a place or memory that evokes a sense of peace and groundedness. This might be a favorite nature spot, a comforting room, or a moment of connection with a loved one. Let the felt sense of this resource permeate your body and mind.

6. Once you've established a felt sense of your somatic anchor, choose a simple word or phrase that encapsulates the experience for you. This might be something like "safe," "grounded," "at peace," or "centered." Repeat this word or phrase to yourself a few times, allowing it to become associated with the embodied state you're cultivating.

7. You can further reinforce your somatic anchor by exploring gestures or postures that evoke a sense of stability and comfort. For example, you might place a hand on your heart, feel your feet firmly rooted on the ground, or gently hug yourself. Experiment with different options and notice which ones resonate most strongly with your anchor state.

8. Allow yourself to rest in this resourced experience for several minutes, savoring the sensations of ease, support, and integration. If your mind wanders or gets caught up in thoughts, gently guide it back to the felt sense of your somatic anchor.

9. When you feel ready to close the practice, take a few deep breaths and slowly open your eyes, letting your gaze be soft and receptive. Please take a moment to appreciate your capacity to generate and access this embodied resource, knowing that it's always available to you when you need it.

Closing

As you complete this practice, take a moment to appreciate the power of your own embodied presence as a source of grounding and resilience. Notice any shifts in your nervous system, perhaps a greater sense of setlines, equilibrium, or self-possession. Consider practicing your somatic anchor on a regular basis, even when you're not feeling dysregulated, to reinforce its stability and accessibility. Over time, you may find that you can call upon this resource with greater ease and speed, allowing you to navigate challenges with more flexibility and grace. Remember, your body is always here as a trusted ally and guide, offering a felt sense of safety and support whenever you need it.

EXERCISE: PROGRESSIVE MUSCLE RELAXATION FOR EMBODIMENT

Progressive Muscle Relaxation (PMR) for Embodiment is an exercise that combines the technique of PMR with mindful awareness to help you cultivate a deeper sense of presence, connection, and integration within your physical body. When we experience stress, trauma, or dissociation, we may feel disconnected or numb to our bodily sensations and experiences, leading to feelings of anxiety, confusion, or emptiness. By systematically tensing and relaxing different muscle groups while bringing gentle attention to the sensations and feelings that arise, we can start to rebuild a sense of safety, trust, and attunement with our embodied experience. This practice invites you to use the tool of PMR to explore and deepen your relationship with your body, and to cultivate a greater sense of wholeness, vitality, and ease within your physical being.

Steps

1. Find a quiet, comfortable space where you can lie down or sit without disturbance. If lying down, use a mat or blanket for support, and consider placing a pillow under your head and knees for added comfort. If sitting, choose a chair or cushion that allows you to feel stable and relaxed, with your feet flat on the floor.

2. Close your eyes and take a few deep breaths, allowing your body to settle and your mind to become present. Notice the sensations of your breath moving in and out, and the gentle rise and fall of your chest and belly.

3. Starting with your feet and toes, gently tense the muscles in this area, scrunching your toes and contracting the soles of your feet. As you tense these muscles, bring your full attention to the sensations that arise, noticing any feelings of tightness, pressure, or warmth.

4. Hold the tension for a few seconds, and then release, allowing your feet and toes to relax completely. As you release the tension, notice any sensations of softening, spreading, or letting go. Take a moment to fully experience the contrast between tension and relaxation in this area of your body.

5. Take a few deep breaths, and then move your attention up to your calves and shins. Again, gently tense the muscles in this area, contracting your calves and lifting your feet slightly off the ground. As you tense these muscles, bring your full attention to the sensations that arise, noticing any feelings of

engagement, activation, or intensity.

6. Hold the tension for a few seconds, and then release, allowing your calves and shins to relax completely. As you release the tension, notice any sensations of heaviness, tingling, or unwinding. Take a moment to fully experience the relief and ease that comes with letting go.

7. Continue this process of tensing, noticing, and releasing each muscle group, moving up through your body in the following sequence: thighs, hips and buttocks, stomach, chest, back, shoulders, arms and hands, neck, and face. For each area, take your time to fully engage the muscles, bringing your complete attention to the sensations that arise, and then releasing completely, savoring the experience of relaxation and release.

8. As you move through the practice, notice if any thoughts, emotions, or memories arise in connection with particular areas of your body. Perhaps you notice a sense of holding or bracing in your stomach, or a feeling of tenderness or vulnerability in your chest. Simply allow these experiences to be present, without judgment or analysis, and continue to breathe and soften into the sensations of your body.

9. When you have completed the PMR sequence, take a few deep breaths and feel the overall sense of relaxation and presence throughout your entire body. Notice any areas that feel especially soft, open, or alive, and any areas that still feel tense, numb, or disconnected.

10. As you rest in this state of embodied awareness, silently offer your body a few words or phrases of kindness and appreciation. You might say something like, "Thank you for all that you do for me," or "I am here with you, listening and loving." Allow yourself to feel a sense of gratitude and compassion for your physical being.

11. Take a few more deep breaths, and then gently begin to wiggle your fingers and toes, bringing small movements back into your body. Slowly open your eyes and take a few moments to reorient to your surroundings, noticing any shifts in your sense of embodiment or presence.

12. As you move through the rest of your day, see if you can maintain a sense of connection and attunement to your physical experience, using the skills of PMR and embodied awareness to navigate any moments of stress, disconnection, or overwhelm.

Conclusion

By combining the technique of PMR with mindful awareness, this practice can help us to release patterns of chronic tension, numbness, or dissociation, and to develop a more loving and attuned relationship with our embodied experience.

Regular practice of PMR for Embodiment can support us in feeling more grounded, centered, and alive in our physical being, and in developing the resilience and capacity to navigate the ups and downs of life with greater ease and grace. It can help us to heal from experiences of trauma, stress, or disconnection, and to cultivate a sense of wholeness, vitality, and belonging within ourselves.

EXERCISE: BREATH-GUIDED EMBODIMENT PRACTICE

Breath-Guided Embodiment Practice is an exercise that combines the power of conscious breathing with mindful body awareness to help you cultivate a deeper sense of presence, connection, and integration within your physical being. Our breath is a powerful anchor for our attention and a gateway to the present moment, and by bringing our awareness to the sensations and movements of breathing, we can start to deepen our relationship with our embodied experience. This practice invites you to use your breath as a guide and a companion for exploring the landscape of your body, and to cultivate a sense of safety, curiosity, and compassion as you journey inward. With each inhale and exhale, you will have the opportunity to awaken new dimensions of feeling, knowing, and being within yourself, and to discover the wisdom and aliveness that reside within your body.

Steps

1. Find a quiet, comfortable space where you can lie down or sit without disturbance. If lying down, use a mat or blanket for support, and consider placing a pillow under your head and knees for added comfort. If sitting, choose a chair or cushion that allows you to feel stable and relaxed, with your feet flat on the floor and your spine upright but not rigid.

2. Close your eyes and take a few deep breaths, allowing your body to settle and your mind to become present. Notice the sensations of your breath moving in and out, and the gentle rise and fall of your chest and belly.

3. Begin to deepen and slow your breath, inhaling through your nose and exhaling through your mouth. Allow your breath to find its own natural rhythm and depth, without forcing or controlling.

4. As you continue to breathe, bring your attention to the physical sensations of breathing in your body. Notice the coolness of the air as it enters your nostrils, and the warmth of the air as it leaves your mouth. Feel the expansion of your ribcage and the release of your belly with each inhale and exhale.

5. Now, begin to expand your awareness to include your whole body, from the top of your head to the tips of your toes. With each inhalation, imagine your breath flowing into a different area of your body, filling it with oxygen, energy, and awareness. With each exhalation, imagine any tension, stagnation, or numbness flowing out of that area, leaving it feeling more open, alive, and connected.

6. Start by bringing your breath to your feet and toes, feeling the sensations of your breath moving into and out of this area. Notice any feelings of warmth, tingling, or pulsing that may arise, and any sense of grounding or connection with the earth beneath you.

7. Slowly move your breath up through your body, bringing your attention to your legs, hips, pelvis, and lower back. As you breathe into each area, notice any sensations of tightness, aching, or holding, and imagine your breath gently softening and releasing any tension or discomfort.

8. Continue to guide your breath through your stomach, chest, upper back, and shoulders, feeling the

rise and fall of your breath in each area. Notice any emotions or memories that may arise as you bring your awareness to these parts of your body, and allow them to be present without getting caught up in their content.

9. Bring your breath to your arms and hands, feeling the flow of energy and sensation from your shoulders to your fingertips. Notice any areas that feel especially alive or sensitive, and any areas that feel numb or disconnected.

10. Finally, bring your breath to your neck, throat, face, and head, feeling the subtle movements of your breath in these areas. Notice any sensations of relaxation or spaciousness that may arise as you bring your awareness to the top of your body.

11. As you complete the practice, take a few deep breaths and feel the overall sense of embodiment and presence throughout your entire being. Notice any shifts in your sense of aliveness, connection, or integration within your body.

12. Gently open your eyes and take a few moments to reorient to your surroundings, carrying the quality of embodied awareness with you as you move through the rest of your day.

Conclusion

Breath-Guided Embodiment Practice was included in this book because it offers a simple yet profound way to deepen our relationship with our physical being and to cultivate a greater sense of presence, connection, and aliveness within ourselves. By using the breath as an anchor and a guide for exploring the sensations and feelings of our body, we can start to release patterns of tension, numbness, or dissociation, and to awaken new dimensions of embodied awareness and vitality.

Regular practice of Breath-Guided Embodiment can support us in developing a more intimate and compassionate relationship with our body, and in cultivating the resilience and resources to navigate the challenges and opportunities of life with greater ease and skill. It can help us to heal from experiences of trauma, neglect, or disconnection, and to discover the wisdom, creativity, and joy that reside within our embodied being.

EXERCISE: HEART-CENTERED EMBODIMENT VISUALIZATION

Heart-Centered Embodiment Visualization is an exercise that combines the power of guided imagery with the wisdom and compassion of the heart to help you cultivate a deeper sense of presence, connection, and integration within your physical being. When we experience stress, trauma, or disconnection, we may feel cut off from the aliveness and intelligence of our body, leading to feelings of anxiety, numbness, or disembodiment. By connecting with the energy and essence of the heart, we can start to bridge the divide between mind and body, and to cultivate a sense of wholeness, healing, and resilience within ourselves. This practice invites you to use the power of visualization to awaken the healing power of your heart, and to infuse your entire being with the qualities of love, compassion, and embodied presence.

Steps

1. Find a quiet, comfortable space where you can sit or lie down without disturbance. If you have access to a heart rate variability biofeedback (HRVB) device, attach it according to the manufacturer's instructions and start the recording process.

2. Close your eyes and take a few deep breaths, allowing your body to settle and your mind to become present. Notice the sensations of your breath moving in and out, and the gentle rise and fall of your chest and belly.

3. Bring your attention to the area of your heart, in the center of your chest. Place one or both hands over your heart, feeling the warmth and texture of your skin beneath your touch.

4. As you focus on your heart, notice any sensations or feelings that arise in this area. You may feel the steady beat of your heart, the expansion and contraction of your chest with each breath, or a sense of openness, tenderness, or vulnerability.

5. Now, begin to imagine that with each inhalation, you are drawing in the energy of love, compassion, and healing into your heart center. Visualize this energy as a warm, golden light, filling your heart with a sense of peace, comfort, and well-being.

6. As you exhale, imagine that you are sending this golden light from your heart to every cell and fiber of your being. Visualize the light flowing down through your torso, infusing your organs and muscles with a sense of warmth, vitality, and aliveness.

7. Continue to breathe in the energy of love and compassion, and breathe out the light of embodiment and healing. With each inhalation, feel your heart expanding and glowing with the radiance of unconditional love. With each exhalation, feel this radiance spreading throughout your entire body, awakening every part of your being to its natural state of wholeness and integration.

8. As you continue this practice, notice if there are any areas of your body that feel especially tight, numb, or disconnected. Imagine sending extra light and love to these areas, inviting them to soften, open, and reconnect with the wisdom and intelligence of your heart.

9. Take a few moments to simply rest in the experience of heart-centered embodiment, feeling the aliveness, presence, and integration that arises when your mind, body, and heart are in harmony and alignment.

10. If at any point you feel ungrounded or overwhelmed, imagine that you can send roots or cords of light from your heart center deep into the earth, anchoring you in a sense of stability, safety, and support.

11. When you feel ready to end the practice, take a few deep breaths and gently open your eyes,

taking a moment to reorient to your surroundings. If you are using an HRVB device, stop the recording and take note of any changes in your heart rate variability or emotional state.

12. Take a moment to reflect on your experience. What did you notice in your body and mind as you practiced heart-centered embodiment? What insights or invitations arose for you? How might you integrate this practice into your daily life, as a way of cultivating greater presence, compassion, and embodied wholeness?

Conclusion

Heart-Centered Embodiment Visualization was included in this book because it offers a powerful way to awaken the healing power of the heart and to cultivate a deeper sense of presence, connection, and integration within our physical being. By using the tool of visualization to infuse our entire body with the energy of love, compassion, and embodied awareness, we can start to heal the divisions between mind, body, and spirit, and to access the innate wisdom and wholeness that reside within us.

Regular practice of Heart-Centered Embodiment Visualization can help us to develop a more loving and compassionate relationship with our body, and to cultivate the resilience and resources needed to navigate the ups and downs of life with greater ease and skill. It can support us in healing from experiences of trauma, neglect, or disembodiment, and in awakening to the aliveness, creativity, and joy that are our birthright as embodied beings.

EXERCISE: BILATERAL STIMULATION FOR GROUNDING

Bilateral Stimulation for Grounding is an exercise that uses the technique of bilateral stimulation, commonly employed in Eye Movement Desensitization and Reprocessing (EMDR) therapy, to help you cultivate a sense of presence, stability, and grounding in the here and now. Bilateral stimulation involves alternating stimulation of the left and right sides of the body, which is thought to facilitate the integration of neural pathways and promote a sense of balance and regulation in the nervous system. By combining bilateral stimulation with mindful attention to the present moment, this practice can help you to anchor yourself in a felt sense of safety and embodiment, and to develop greater resilience in the face of stress, anxiety, or overwhelm.

Steps

1. Find a quiet, comfortable space where you can sit or stand without disturbance. If sitting, choose a chair or cushion that allows you to feel stable and supported, with your feet flat on the ground. If standing, find a position that feels balanced and grounded, with your feet hip-width apart.

2. Close your eyes or maintain a soft, unfocused gaze. Take a few deep breaths, allowing your body to settle and your mind to become present.

3. Choose a form of bilateral stimulation that feels comfortable and accessible for you. Some options include:

- Tapping your knees or thighs alternately with your hands
- Crossing your arms in front of your chest and tapping your shoulders alternately
- Tapping your feet alternately on the ground
- Moving your eyes from side to side, tracking your gaze across the room
- Listening to alternating tones or sounds in your left and right ears (requires headphones)

4. Begin your chosen form of bilateral stimulation, setting a slow, steady rhythm that feels grounding and regulating for your nervous system. As you engage in the stimulation, bring your attention to the physical sensations of the movement or sound, noticing the alternating activation of the left and right sides of your body.

5. As you continue the bilateral stimulation, begin to expand your awareness to include your entire body and your surroundings. Notice the points of contact between your body and the surface beneath you, feeling the support and stability of the ground or chair. Notice any sensations of tension or ease in your muscles, and any feelings of warmth or coolness on your skin.

6. If your mind begins to wander or get caught up in thoughts, gently redirect your attention back to the physical sensations of the bilateral stimulation and your body in the present moment. You may find it helpful to silently repeat a grounding phrase or affirmation, such as "I am here now," or "I am safe and supported."

7. Continue the bilateral stimulation for several minutes, allowing yourself to sink deeper into the experience of embodied presence and grounding. Notice any shifts in your sense of calm, clarity, or connection to the present moment.

8. If at any point you feel ungrounded or overwhelmed, take a few deep breaths and feel your feet firmly planted on the ground. You may also want to open your eyes and take in your surroundings, reminding yourself that you are safe and supported in the here and now.

9. When you feel ready to end the practice, slowly bring the bilateral stimulation to a close and take a few deep breaths. Notice any sensations of stillness, ease, or integration in your body and mind.

10. Gently open your eyes and take a few moments to reorient to your surroundings. Notice any changes in your sense of groundedness, presence, or resilience.

11. Take a moment to reflect on your experience. What did you notice in your body and mind as you engaged in bilateral stimulation? What insights or invitations arose for you? How might you integrate this practice into your daily life, as a resource for grounding and self-regulation?

Conclusion

Bilateral Stimulation for Grounding was included in this book because it offers a simple yet powerful tool for cultivating embodied presence, self-regulation, and resilience. By using the technique of bilateral stimulation to promote balance and integration in the nervous system, and combining this with mindful attention to the present moment, this practice can help us to anchor ourselves in a felt sense of safety and stability, even in the face of stress or challenge.

Regular practice of Bilateral Stimulation for Grounding can support us in developing a more grounded and resilient relationship with ourselves and the world around us, and in navigating the ups and downs of life with greater ease and skill. It can be particularly helpful for individuals who struggle with anxiety, dissociation, or trauma-related symptoms, as it provides a concrete and embodied way to regulate the nervous system and stay connected to the present moment.

16. TRAUMA HEALING THROUGH THE BODY

Trauma is a deeply embodied experience that leaves an indelible mark on every aspect of our being. When we endure a traumatic event, our bodies undergo a complex series of physiological changes designed to help us survive the immediate threat. Our heart rate accelerates, blood pressure rises, and muscles tense in preparation for a fight or flight. Our perceptions sharpen and intensify, making us hypervigilant to any signs of danger in our environment.

These instinctive survival responses are a powerful testament to the wisdom and resilience of our bodies, reminding us of our innate capacity to protect and defend ourselves in the face of overwhelming stress or adversity. However, when the traumatic event has passed, these survival responses often linger, becoming encoded in our bodies as procedural memories—deeply ingrained patterns of physical tension, arousal, and reactivity that can persist long after the original danger has subsided.

For many trauma survivors, these stuck survival responses can become a chronic source of suffering and distress. They may feel constantly on edge, jumpy, and reactive to even the slightest triggers. They may grapple with feelings of helplessness, shame, or rage as their bodies continue to react as if the traumatic event is still occurring in the present moment. They may feel disconnected from their physical sensations and emotions as if their bodies have become a foreign and frightening landscape.

UNDERSTANDING TRAUMA

To fully grasp the impact of trauma on the body, it is essential to recognize that trauma can take many forms and arise from a variety of experiences. Two primary categories of trauma are emotional trauma and physical trauma.

Understanding Emotional Trauma

Emotional trauma refers to the psychological impact of a deeply distressing or disturbing event. It can result from experiences such as abuse, neglect, abandonment, betrayal, or the loss of a loved one. Other examples of experiences that can lead to emotional trauma include witnessing violence, experiencing discrimination, or surviving a natural disaster. Emotional trauma can shatter our sense of safety, trust, and self-worth, leaving us feeling vulnerable, anxious, and disconnected from others.

The effects of emotional trauma can be pervasive and long-lasting, impacting our relationships, our ability to regulate our emotions, and our overall sense of well-being. Symptoms may include chronic anxiety, depression, panic attacks, difficulty concentrating, and a sense of numbness or detachment from our feelings. Emotional trauma can also have a significant impact on a person's self-esteem, leading to feelings of worthlessness, shame, and self-doubt. It can affect interpersonal relationships, making it difficult for individuals to trust others, form close bonds, or maintain healthy boundaries.

Overall, emotional trauma can greatly diminish a person's quality of life, interfering with their ability to work, study, or engage in meaningful activities.

Understanding Physical Trauma

Physical trauma refers to bodily injuries or harm resulting from accidents, assaults, or medical procedures. It can range from minor cuts and bruises to severe, life-threatening injuries. Physical trauma can be a single incident or repeated occurrences, such as in cases of domestic violence or child abuse.

The impact of physical trauma extends beyond the visible wounds and scars. It can lead to chronic pain, reduced mobility, and a heightened state of physical arousal and reactivity. The body may remain in a constant state of high alert, prepared for the next threat or injury. This persistent state of hypervigilance can be exhausting and debilitating, making it difficult to relax, sleep, or engage in normal daily activities. Physical trauma can also lead to long-term physical health problems, such as chronic headaches, gastrointestinal issues, or persistent pain in the affected areas.

Furthermore, physical trauma can also lead to emotional trauma, particularly if the injury was caused by violence or abuse. The psychological impact of physical trauma can be just as significant as the physical consequences, leading to feelings of fear, helplessness, and vulnerability. In some cases, individuals may develop post-traumatic stress disorder (PTSD) because of the traumatic event, which can further compound the emotional and physical challenges they face.

HOW SOMATIC THERAPY APPLIES TO EMOTIONAL AND PHYSICAL TRAUMA

Somatic therapy is a holistic approach to healing that recognizes the interconnectedness of the mind and body. It is based on the understanding that trauma is not just a psychological phenomenon but also a physiological one and that true healing must address both the emotional and physical aspects of the traumatic experience.

The key principles of somatic therapy include:

1. Focusing on the mind-body connection: Somatic therapy recognizes that our thoughts, emotions, and physical sensations are all interconnected and that trauma can disrupt this delicate balance. By bringing awareness to the body and its sensations, somatic therapy aims to help individuals reconnect with their physical experience and develop a greater sense of integration between their mind and body.

2. Regulating the nervous system: Trauma can cause dysregulation in the nervous system, leading to states of hyperarousal or hypo arousal. Somatic therapy uses various techniques to help regulate the nervous system, such as grounding exercises, breath work, and sensory awareness, in order to promote a sense of safety and stability in the body.

3. Using body-based interventions: Somatic therapy employs a range of body-based interventions, such as movement, touch, and sound, to help individuals release stored tension, process emotions, and develop new patterns of embodiment. These interventions are designed to work with the body's natural healing mechanisms and promote a sense of agency and empowerment.

For individuals with emotional trauma, somatic therapy can be particularly helpful in releasing stored emotions and developing a greater sense of safety and control in their bodies. By bringing awareness to physical sensations and using body-based interventions, individuals can learn to regulate their nervous system, reduce symptoms of anxiety and depression, and develop a more positive relationship with their emotions. Somatic therapy can also help individuals establish healthy boundaries, improve their self-esteem, and cultivate a greater sense of self-compassion.

For individuals with physical trauma, somatic therapy can help to release chronic tension, improve mobility and flexibility, and develop a more positive relationship with their bodies. By working with the body's natural healing mechanisms, somatic therapy can help to reduce pain, improve circulation, and promote overall physical well-being. Additionally, somatic therapy can help individuals process any emotional trauma associated with their physical injury, reducing symptoms of PTSD, and promoting a greater sense of integration and wholeness.

It is important to note that somatic therapy is a collaborative process between the therapist and the client. A trained somatic therapist can provide a safe and supportive environment for individuals to explore their embodied experience while also offering guidance and expertise in working with trauma. The therapist can help individuals develop a greater sense of self-awareness, self-regulation, and self-compassion while also providing tools and techniques for managing symptoms and promoting healing.

Regardless of the type of trauma experienced, the body plays a leading role in both the experience and the healing of trauma. In somatic healing, the key to resolving stuck trauma responses lies in working directly with the body itself. By gently and skillfully inviting our bodies to complete the instinctive defensive actions that were thwarted or overridden during the original traumatic event, we can help discharge the stuck survival energy and restore a sense of safety and equilibrium to our system.

THE ROLE OF INSTINCTIVE TRAUMA RESPONSES

To understand how this process works, it is helpful to examine the different instinctive survival responses that can arise during a traumatic event, often referred to as the "four F's" of trauma: fight, flight, freeze, and submit.

- The fight response is characterized by feelings of anger and aggression and a powerful urge to confront or eliminate the source of the threat. It is accompanied by physical sensations of tension, heat, and a rush of energy.

- The flight response is characterized by feelings of fear, panic, and an overwhelming desire to escape or run away from the threatening situation. It is accompanied by physical sensations of trembling, heart palpitations, and tunnel vision.
- The freeze response is more complex, involving elements of both fight and flight. In the initial stages, our bodies may become temporarily immobilized as we assess the situation and prepare for action, accompanied by physical sensations of coldness, numbness, and a sense of time slowing down or standing still. If the freeze response persists, it can lead to a state of tonic immobility—a "playing dead" response in which our bodies become completely shut down and unresponsive, often accompanied by feelings of dissociation, detachment, and a sense of being trapped or helpless.
- The submit response is characterized by feelings of helplessness and despair and a sense of giving up or giving in to the overwhelming power of the threat. It is accompanied by physical sensations of heaviness and collapse and a profound lack of energy or motivation.

Many trauma survivors may experience elements of all four responses at different points during a traumatic event. These survival responses represent our bodies' best attempts to protect us from harm and ensure our survival. However, problems arise when they become stuck or frozen in our bodies long after the original threat has passed, leading to chronic states of hyperarousal or hypo arousal.

ALLOWING IMPULSES FOR COMPLETION

To work with these stuck survival responses and invite them towards resolution and completion, somatic trauma healing employs the principle of titration—working with small, manageable doses of traumatic activation rather than trying to force a cathartic release all at once. This approach is necessary because traumatic activation can be incredibly overwhelming and destabilizing for the nervous system, and attempting to confront it head-on can often lead to re-traumatization or further dissociation.

One way to work with titration is through the practice of "discharging"—allowing our bodies to complete the instinctive defensive actions that were thwarted or overridden during the original traumatic event. For example, suppose someone experienced the urge to fight back during an assault but was unable to do so. In that case, they may need to find safe and controlled ways to express that fighting energy, such as hitting a pillow or yelling into a cushion. Similarly, if someone experienced the urge to flee during a traumatic event but was trapped or restrained, they may need to find ways to allow their bodies to complete that flight response, such as through running, dancing, or shaking out their limbs.

The key is to work slowly and gently, staying within our "window of tolerance"—the range of activation that feels manageable and safe for our nervous system. As we allow these instinctive defensive responses to complete themselves, we may notice physical and emotional shifts occurring in our bodies, such as trembling, shaking, or other involuntary movements, as well as waves of emotion like fear, anger, or grief coming to the surface to be expressed and released.

Over time, as we continue to work with these discharging practices, we may start to notice a profound shift in our overall sense of safety and equilibrium, finding that triggers that once sent us spiraling into states of terror or dissociation no longer hold the same charge.

Somatic trauma healing is a complex and non-linear process that requires patience, persistence, and support, as well as a deep commitment to our growth and transformation. However, the rewards are immeasurable. As we begin to unfreeze our stuck survival responses and restore a sense of safety and vitality to our bodies, we open new possibilities for healing, connection, and joy in every area of our lives, reclaiming our birthright as embodied, empowered beings.

Somatic trauma healing invites us to rewrite the story of our bodies, transforming the legacy of pain and fear into a narrative of strength, compassion, and resilience. It reminds us that no matter how lost or broken we may feel, our bodies hold an innate intelligence and capacity for healing that can never be fully extinguished. By learning to listen to and trust the wisdom of our bodies, we begin to discover a new sense of wholeness and integration, a felt sense of being at home in our skin.

EXERCISE: COMPLETING SURVIVAL RESPONSES

When we experience overwhelming stress or trauma, our bodies can get stuck in survival responses like fight, flight, or freeze. These instinctive defensive reactions are designed to protect us from threats, but if they do not complete fully, they can leave residual activation and tension in the body. This practice offers a safe, titrated way to process and release blocked survival energy, allowing the nervous system to return to a state of regulation and ease. It is important to approach this work gradually, ensuring ample time for resourcing and stabilization. Remember, the goal is not to re-traumatize or overwhelm but to gently invite the body to complete its natural self-protective responses.

Guided Instructions

1. Begin by preparing a safe, private space where you can move freely without obstruction. Remove any furniture or objects that might impede your movement or cause injury. Ensure that you have plenty of time and will not be disturbed.

2. Before engaging with any survival responses, spend ample time resourcing through grounding breathwork and embodiment practices. You might place a hand on your heart or belly, feeling the steady rhythm of your breath. Or you could imagine a sense of roots extending from your body into the earth, anchoring you in a felt sense of stability and support.

3. Once you feel sufficiently resourced, bring your attention to any areas of your body where you notice tension, bracing, or a sense of "tightness." These may be places where survival energy is being held, waiting for an opportunity for release.

4. Gently invite any small, unconscious movements related to these activated areas to arise. This

might look like a slight trembling in your legs, a subtle clenching of your fists, or a gentle rocking motion. Allow these movements to emerge without judgment or force.

5. If it feels safe and authentic, give the survival movements permission to intensify and evolve. You might find yourself needing to push, kick, or run in place. Or you might feel an impulse to curl up into a ball or hide. Trust the wisdom of your body and let the responses unfold organically.

6. You can incorporate sounds, vocalizations, or rocking motions to support the release process. Let yourself growl, yell, or whimper if it feels right. Experiment with different rhythms and pacing, following the natural ebb and flow of the survival energy.

7. Throughout the practice, remember to pendulate between activation and settling. After allowing a survival response to complete, take a few moments to re-ground and re-resource. Notice any shifts in your bodily sensations and any sense of relief, lightness, or spaciousness.

8. If you feel overwhelmed or disconnected at any point, prioritize resourcing and stabilization over processing. Return to your grounding practices or take a break and return to the exercise later. Trust that your system knows its timing and capacity for release.

Closing

As you complete this practice, take a moment to honor your body's innate wisdom and resilience. Recognize that by allowing your survival responses to be fully expressed and released, you are supporting your nervous system's natural capacity for healing and self-regulation. Consider integrating this type of titrated release work into your ongoing self-care routine, either on your own or with the guidance of a trained trauma-informed practitioner. Remember, the path of embodied healing is a gradual, nonlinear process that requires patience, compassion, and a deep trust in the intelligence of your Being. With each cycle of resourcing and release, you are strengthening your capacity to move through the world with greater ease, vitality, and wholeness.

EXERCISE: TRAUMA-SENSITIVE YOGA POSES

Yoga can be a powerful somatic practice for cultivating embodied presence, self-regulation, and resilience. However, for those with a history of trauma, certain poses or approaches to yoga can feel dysregulating or overwhelming. This practice offers a selection of beginner-friendly, trauma-sensitive yoga poses that you can explore gently and mindfully. The emphasis is on cultivating a sense of internal safety, choice, and attunement rather than striving for any physical outcome. Remember, the goal is not to achieve the "perfect" pose but to use the postures as opportunities to deepen your relationship with your own embodied experience.

Guided Instructions

1. Begin by finding a safe, comfortable space where you can move around freely. This might be a quiet corner of your home, a dedicated yoga room, or even a peaceful outdoor spot. Ensure that the space

feels conducive to relaxation and self-connection.

2. Take a few slow, grounding breaths, allowing your awareness to settle into your body. Notice the sensation of your feet on the ground, the weight of your body supported by the earth beneath you. Invite a sense of rootedness and stability.

3. When you feel ready, explore one or more of the following trauma-sensitive yoga poses:

- **Child's Pose:** Come to a kneeling position, then slowly fold forward, bringing your forehead towards the ground. You can rest your arms alongside your body or extend them in front of you. This pose can be deeply calming and grounding.
- **Cat/Cow:** Start on your hands and knees, with your wrists under your shoulders and your knees under your hips. As you inhale, arch your back, and lift your head and tailbone towards the sky (Cow Pose). As you exhale, round your spine and tuck your chin towards your chest (Cat Pose). Move fluidly between these two poses, following the natural rhythm of your breath.
- **Seated Spinal Twist:** Sit on the floor with your legs extended in front of you. Bend your right knee and place your right foot on the outside of your left thigh. Place your right hand on the floor behind you and your left hand on your right knee. Gently twist to the right, keeping your spine long and your shoulders relaxed. Hold for a few breaths, then release and repeat on the other side.

4. As you explore each pose, bring a sense of curiosity and openness to your internal experience. Notice any physical sensations, emotions, or thoughts that arise without judgment or interpretation. Allow your breath to be your anchor, guiding you back to the present moment.

5. Use your breath to find a sense of expansion and release in each posture. Imagine that you are creating space in your body with each inhalation and softening into that space with each exhalation. Let your breath be a source of nourishment and ease.

6. Remember, there is no need to force or strain in any pose. If you encounter any sense of activation or discomfort, simply back off and return to a neutral position. Trust your body's wisdom and only go as far as feels safe and supportive of you.

Closing

As you complete this practice, take a moment to acknowledge your body's innate wisdom and resilience. Notice any shifts in your nervous system, perhaps a greater sense of calm, clarity, or embodied presence. Consider integrating these trauma-sensitive yoga poses into your regular self-care routine to cultivate a deeper sense of safety, attunement, and regulation in your body. Remember, the path of embodied healing is a gradual, nonlinear process that requires patience, self-compassion, and a willingness to honor your own unique needs and boundaries. Trust that with each mindful breath and each gentle movement, you are strengthening your capacity to navigate the terrain of your inner landscape with greater ease, compassion, and grace.

EXERCISE: THERAPEUTIC TREMORING

Therapeutic tremoring, also known as neurogenic tremors or shaking, is a natural mechanism that the body uses to release pent-up stress, tension, and survival energy. When animals in the wild experience a life-threatening situation, they often shake and tremble after the danger has passed, allowing their nervous system to reset and return to a state of balance. For humans, intentionally evoking and allowing these tremors can be a potent way to discharge stored trauma and restore a sense of embodied safety. This practice can be intense and cathartic, as it involves unshackling deeply held patterns of bracing and control. As such, it requires proper resourcing, titration, and often the guidance of a trained practitioner.

Guided Instructions

1. Begin by preparing a safe, comfortable space where you can move and vocalize freely. Remove any furniture or objects that might obstruct your movement or cause injury. Ensure that the area is private and that you will not be disturbed.

2. Before initiating any tremoring, spend ample time resourcing and grounding through breathwork and body awareness practices. You might place a hand on your lower belly, feeling the steady rise and fall of your breath. Or you could visualize a golden light filling your body, bringing a sense of warmth, security, and ease.

3. When you feel sufficiently resourced, begin to gently shake your hands and arms as if you were flicking water off your fingertips. Allow the movement to be loose and relaxed, without any rhythm or intensity. Notice any sensations of vibration or tingling that arise.

4. As you continue to shake your arms, invite the tremors to spread throughout your entire body. You might feel your legs begin to tremble, your torso gently quiver, or your jaw softly chatters. Allow these movements to arise organically without forcing or controlling them.

5. If it feels natural, you can incorporate sounds or vocalizations to further facilitate the release process. Let yourself sigh, moan, or even scream if the impulse arises. Trust the wisdom of your body and allow the expressions to move through you freely.

6. Throughout the practice, remember to go slowly and prioritize resourcing between waves of tremoring. If you feel overwhelmed or disconnected at any point, pause, and return to your grounding practices. Place a hand on your heart, take a few deep breaths, or gently rock your body from side to side.

7. As you become more comfortable with the tremoring process, you can explore incorporating dynamic movements like gentle bouncing, shaking, or even jumping up and down. Let these movements be playful and spontaneous, following the natural impulses of your body.

8. When you feel complete, take a few minutes to rest in stillness, noticing any shifts in your physical, emotional, and energetic state. You may feel a sense of lightness, openness, or relief. You may also feel

tender or vulnerable, which is a natural part of the release process.

Closing

As you complete this practice, take a moment to honor your body's innate capacity for self-regulation and healing. Recognize that by allowing your tremors to move through you, you are supporting your nervous system's natural ability to discharge excess energy and find a state of greater balance and resilience. Consider integrating therapeutic tremoring into your ongoing self-care routine, either on your own or with the support of a skilled somatic practitioner. Remember, the path of embodied trauma resolution is a courageous and deeply personal journey that requires patience, self-compassion, and a willingness to trust the intelligence of your body. With each shake, tremor, and release, you are reclaiming your birthright of wholeness, vitality, and authentic self-expression.

EXERCISE: EMDR-INSPIRED BILATERAL STIMULATION FOR TRAUMA PROCESSING

Eye Movement Desensitization and Reprocessing (EMDR) is a well-established psychotherapy approach used to treat symptoms stemming from disturbing or traumatic life experiences. One key component of EMDR involves bilateral stimulation, usually in the form of side-to-side eye movements, while the client focuses on a distressing memory. This bilateral stimulation is thought to facilitate the brain's natural adaptive information processing mechanisms, helping memories become less vivid and emotionally charged over time.

This exercise offers an EMDR-inspired technique using bilateral stimulation that can be self-administered as a way to begin processing distressing memories or experiences in a gradual, titrated manner. By bringing the disturbing memory to mind while engaging in bilateral stimulation, the emotional intensity associated with the memory may start to diminish. It's important to note that this exercise is not a substitute for working with a trained EMDR therapist, especially for severe trauma. However, it can be a helpful self-administered tool for processing milder distressing memories in a safe, measured way.

Steps

1. Identify a mildly to moderately distressing memory, image, or belief that you feel emotionally ready and well-resourced enough to process. It's advisable to start with less intense targets and work up to more disturbing ones only when you feel equipped to do so.

2. Find a quiet, private place where you can sit comfortably without interruption. Take a few slow, deep breaths, grounding yourself in the present moment. Notice your body in the chair and your feet on the floor.

3. Bring the distressing memory to mind. Notice any images, beliefs, emotions, or body sensations that arise as you focus on it. If it feels too intense at any point, open your eyes, return to the present, and

ground yourself before proceeding. You are in control of the process.

4. Choose a form of bilateral stimulation:

- Eye movements: Visually track your finger or an object as you slowly move it from side to side, letting your eyes follow.
- Tapping: Cross your arms and alternately tap each side of your upper arms or shoulders.
- Sounds: Listen to bilateral alternating tones using headphones.

5. While holding the memory in mind, begin the bilateral stimulation (eye movements, tapping, or sounds) for around 30 seconds or so.

6. Take a deep breath and check in with yourself. Notice if there have been any changes in the images, beliefs, emotions or body sensations related to the memory. There is no right or wrong way to respond - just observe with openness and curiosity.

7. If the distress has not reduced, do another set of bilateral stimulation while focusing on the memory. Check in again, noticing any changes. Repeat for a few sets.

8. If at any point you feel overwhelmed, stop the stimulation, open your eyes, and ground yourself in the present using deep breathing or sensory awareness. You can always take a break or stop the exercise entirely if needed.

9. When the memory feels less intense or your mind naturally shifts to more adaptive information (e.g. reminders of your resilience, support, or safety), you can end the session. Take a few deep breaths and re-orient yourself to your current surroundings.

10. After the exercise, engage in some self-care activities that help you feel grounded and restored, such as taking a walk, drinking tea, journaling, or talking to a supportive friend. Notice any positive shifts in perspective that may have emerged.

Conclusion

EMDR-Inspired Bilateral Stimulation for Trauma Processing was included in this book as a self-help tool for beginning to process mildly to moderately distressing memories or experiences. By combining a focus on the disturbing memory with bilateral stimulation, this exercise aims to jumpstart the brain's natural healing mechanisms, helping to reduce the emotional charge of the memory over time.

While this technique can be a helpful adjunct to therapy or a self-administered exercise for milder memories, it is not a replacement for working with a qualified EMDR therapist, especially for more severe trauma. Trauma processing can be destabilizing, so it's important to only use this exercise if you feel stable, well-resourced, and equipped to tolerate some emotional discomfort.

EXERCISE: SOMATIC EXPERIENCING FOR TRAUMA RELEASE

Somatic Experiencing (SE) is a body-oriented approach to healing trauma that focuses on gently releasing traumatic activation and restoring a sense of safety, balance, and resilience in the nervous system. Developed by Dr. Peter Levine, SE recognizes that trauma is stored in the body as incomplete survival responses, such as fight, flight, or freeze, and that these responses can become stuck or dysregulated, leading to a range of physical, emotional, and psychological symptoms. By bringing mindful attention to the body's sensations and experiences, and by titrating or gradually discharging the traumatic activation, SE aims to help individuals complete and integrate their survival responses, and to restore a sense of embodied safety and vitality. This exercise offers a simplified introduction to some of the key principles and practices of SE, inviting you to explore your body's responses to stress and trauma with curiosity, compassion, and care.

Steps

1. Find a quiet, comfortable space where you can sit or lie down without disturbance. Take a few moments to arrive in your body, noticing the sensations of your breath and the points of contact between your body and the surface beneath you.

2. Begin to scan your body slowly and gently, starting at the top of your head and moving down to the tips of your toes. As you scan, notice any areas of tension, tightness, or discomfort, as well as any areas of relaxation, ease, or comfort. Allow yourself to be present with these sensations, without trying to change or judge them.

3. As you scan, notice if there are any particular sensations or experiences that feel linked to stress, anxiety, or trauma. These may include feelings of constriction, numbness, trembling, or collapse, as well as emotions such as fear, anger, or helplessness. Take a moment to acknowledge these experiences with kindness and respect, recognizing that they are a natural response to overwhelming or threatening events.

4. Choose one area of your body where you notice some activation or discomfort, and bring your attention there. Notice the specific qualities of the sensation, such as its size, shape, temperature, or intensity. See if you can be present with the sensation, breathing into it and allowing it to be there, without getting caught up in the story or meaning behind it.

5. As you focus on the sensation, notice if there are any subtle shifts or changes that occur. The sensation may intensify, soften, expand, or move to a different part of your body. Allow yourself to track these changes with curiosity and openness, trusting your body's natural wisdom and intelligence.

6. If the sensation becomes too intense or overwhelming, see if you can find a place of relative comfort or ease in your body, such as your feet on the ground, your back against a chair, or your hands resting on your belly. Use this felt sense of support and stability to help you regulate and ground yourself,

breathing into it and allowing it to anchor you in the present moment.

7. As you continue to track the sensations in your body, notice if there are any impulses or movements that want to happen, such as shaking, trembling, or shifting position. Rather than forcing or controlling these movements, see if you can allow them to unfold naturally and organically, following your body's lead and letting go of any judgment or expectation.

8. If you notice any emotions or memories arising in connection with the sensations, acknowledge them with compassion and care, without getting lost in their content. Remember that these experiences are a natural part of the healing process, and that they do not define who you are or limit your potential for growth and change.

9. As you near the end of the practice, take a few moments to notice any shifts or changes in your overall sense of embodiment, ease, or resilience. Notice if there are any areas of your body that feel more open, alive, or integrated, and any areas that still feel tense, numb, or disconnected.

10. When you feel ready to conclude the practice, take a few deep breaths and gently open your eyes, taking a moment to reorient to your surroundings. Notice any insights or reflections that may have emerged, and any invitations for further exploration or self-care.

11. Remember that Somatic Experiencing is a gradual and ongoing process, and that it may take time and patience to fully release and integrate the effects of trauma. Be gentle and compassionate with yourself, and trust in your body's innate capacity for healing and wholeness.

Conclusion

Somatic Experiencing for Trauma Release was included in this book because it offers a gentle, effective, and empowering approach to healing trauma through the wisdom of the body. By bringing mindful attention to the body's sensations and experiences, and by gradually discharging and completing survival responses, SE can help individuals to release traumatic activation, regulate their nervous system, and restore a sense of embodied safety and resilience.

Regular practice of SE principles and techniques can support individuals in developing a more attuned and compassionate relationship with their bodies, and in cultivating the internal resources and skills needed to navigate the challenges and stresses of life. It can also help to reduce symptoms of PTSD, anxiety, depression, and chronic pain, and to promote overall feelings of well-being, vitality, and connection.

PART V: INTEGRATION AND RESILIENCE

17. CULTIVATING RADICAL SELF-COMPASSION

On the journey of embodied healing and growth, perhaps no more transformative or essential practice is the cultivation of radical self-compassion. At its core, self-compassion is the act of treating ourselves with the same kindness, care and understanding that we would offer to a beloved friend or family member. It is the practice of learning to relate to ourselves with gentleness, patience, and unconditional positive regard, even during our struggles, failures, and imperfections.

For many of us, the idea of self-compassion can feel foreign or even indulgent. We may have grown up in families or cultures that prioritized self-criticism and judgment as the primary motivators for change and growth, internalizing the belief that being hard on ourselves is the only way to stay disciplined, productive, and successful in life.

However, as we delve deeper into the world of somatic healing, we begin to understand that this kind of self-aggression is not only ineffective but counterproductive to our well-being and flourishing. When we constantly berate ourselves for our perceived shortcomings or mistakes, we activate the body's threat-defense system, flooding our system with stress hormones and creating a state of chronic tension and contraction. Over time, this self-judgment can take a profound toll on our physical, emotional, and relational health, trapping us in cycles of anxiety, depression, or shame and making it difficult to access the inner resources and resilience we need to navigate life's challenges with skill and grace.

THE TRANSFORMATIVE POWER OF SELF-COMPASSION

In contrast, cultivating an attitude of radical self-compassion creates a profound shift in our relationship with ourselves and the world around us. By learning to meet our suffering with tenderness and care, we send a powerful message to our body and mind that we are safe, worthy, and deserving of love and support.

One of the key insights of somatic healing is that our bodies respond to self-compassion in much the same way they would respond to receiving care and support from a trusted friend or loved one. When we offer ourselves words of kindness, soothing touch, or gentle encouragement, we activate the body's "care circuit"—a complex network of neural and hormonal pathways that promote feelings of safety, connection, and well-being, mediated by the release of oxytocin, a powerful hormone that reduces stress, lowers blood pressure, and promotes feelings of bonding and attachment.

As we deepen our practice of self-compassion, we may find that we are able to weather life's storms with greater ease and equanimity, discovering a new sense of inner strength and resilience, a felt sense of being held and supported by a loving presence that is always with us, no matter what challenges we face.

One powerful way to cultivate self-compassion is through the practice of loving-kindness meditation, also known as Metta meditation, which involves silently repeating phrases of goodwill and care towards ourselves and others, such as "may I be happy, may I be healthy, may I be safe, may I live with ease." As we repeat these phrases with sincere intention, we begin to soften the barriers of judgment and resistance that keep us stuck in patterns of self-aggression and suffering, developing a felt sense of being held in a larger field of compassion and care.

Another potent self-compassion practice is the use of soothing self-touch, such as placing a hand on our heart or belly when we are feeling overwhelmed or distressed. This simple gesture can have a profound impact on our nervous system, sending a signal of safety and care to our body and mind. As we learn to offer ourselves these small moments of tenderness and support throughout our day, we begin to rewire our brain and body for greater resilience and well-being, developing a more secure and loving attachment to ourselves.

Of course, the practice of self-compassion is not always easy or comfortable. It requires us to confront the deep-seated beliefs and patterns that have kept us trapped in cycles of self-judgment and suffering and to take responsibility for our healing and growth. It asks us to be willing to sit with the discomfort of our pain and struggle and to trust in the transformative power of love and care.

But as we deepen our commitment to this practice, we may find that it becomes an essential part of our embodied healing journey, the bedrock upon which all other growth and transformation can take place. When we learn to treat ourselves with radical compassion and care, we open new possibilities for healing, connection, and joy in every area of our lives. We experience a sense of wholeness and integration, a felt sense of being at home in our skin and in the world around us.

EXERCISE: LOVING-KINDNESS MEDITATION

Loving-kindness meditation, also known as Metta meditation, is a heart-centered practice that involves extending compassion and goodwill towards oneself and others. By consciously cultivating feelings of warmth, care, and interconnectedness, we can begin to soften the barriers of fear, judgment, and isolation that often keep us locked in patterns of defense and disconnect. This somatic experience of loving-kindness can be particularly nourishing for those who have experienced relational trauma or attachment wounds, as it gently re-wires the nervous system for greater experiences of safety, attunement, and belonging. With regular practice, loving-kindness meditation can become a potent resource for self-soothing, co-regulation, and building secure, harmonious bonds.

Guided Instructions

1. Begin by finding a comfortable seated posture, one that allows you to feel both alert and relaxed. You might sit cross-legged on a cushion or in a chair with your feet planted on the ground. Ensure that your spine is relatively upright, your shoulders are relaxed, and your hands are resting gently on your thighs.

2. Take a few slow, calming breaths, allowing your awareness to settle into the present moment. Notice the sensations of your body contacting the support beneath you and the gentle flow of your breath moving in and out.

3. Now, call to mind the image of someone who naturally evokes feelings of love, warmth, and affection. This could be a dear friend, a family member, a mentor, or even a beloved pet. Visualize them as vividly as you can, noticing the details of their face, their eyes, and their smile.

4. As you hold this image in your heart, tune into the embodied sensations that arise. You might feel a warm glow in your chest, a softening around your eyes and jaw, or a sense of expansiveness and ease throughout your body. Allow yourself to marinate in the felt sense of connection and care.

5. Silently, begin to extend phrases of loving-kindness towards yourself, using the image of your loved one as a source of inspiration. You might say, "May I be safe, may I be happy, may I be healthy, may I live with ease." Repeat these phrases several times, letting the words resonate through your body and mind.

6. Now, expand your circle of loving-kindness to include the person you visualized. Extend the same heartfelt wishes to them, silently repeating, "May you be safe, may you be happy, may you be healthy, may you live with ease." Feel the warmth and care flowing between you, a resonant field of mutual well-wishing.

7. Gradually widen your circle of compassion to encompass other beloved friends and family members. One by one, bring them to mind and include them in your phrases of loving-kindness. Sense the network of care and support that surrounds you, a web of interconnection and goodwill.

8. Continue to expand your field of loving-kindness to include your wider community, your neighbors, acquaintances, and even strangers you pass on the street. Extend your wishes of safety, happiness, health, and ease to all beings without exception. Feel your heart growing more open and inclusive with each expansion.

9. Throughout the practice, keep anchoring your awareness in the somatic sensations of warmth, softness, and care. Notice how your body responds to these expressions of loving-kindness and any shifts in your nervous system towards greater experiences of safety, connection, and ease.

Closing

As you complete this practice, take a moment to rest in the afterglow of your own boundless heart. Notice any shifts in your internal landscape, perhaps a greater sense of spaciousness, tenderness, or belonging. Consider integrating loving-kindness meditation into your daily routine, even if just for a few minutes at a time. Over time, you may find that your capacity for self-compassion, empathy, and attuned connection naturally deepens and expands. Remember, the path of loving-kindness is a lifelong journey, one that invites us to keep meeting ourselves and others with fresh eyes and an open heart. With each practice, you are planting seeds of love, understanding, and relational healing that will blossom in your life and the world around you.

EXERCISE: COMPASSIONATE SELF-TOUCH

Compassionate self-touch is a simple yet powerful practice for cultivating self-attunement, acceptance, and care. By engaging in loving physical contact with our bodies, we send a direct message of safety, worthiness, and belonging to our nervous system. This embodied gesture of kindness can be particularly helpful for those who struggle with harsh self-criticism, neglect, or shame, as it provides a felt sense of being seen, held, and valued. With regular practice, compassionate self-touch can become a reliable resource for self-soothing, emotional regulation, and instilling a deep sense of self-love.

Guided Instructions

1. Begin by finding a comfortable posture, either seated or lying down. Choose a position that allows you to feel relaxed and at ease while still maintaining a sense of presence and dignity. You might sit cross-legged on a cushion or lie on your back with your arms resting gently by your sides.

2. Take a few slow, grounding breaths, allowing your awareness to settle into the present moment. Notice the sensations of your body contacting the surface beneath you and the gentle rise and fall of your chest with each breath.

3. Now, call to mind an intention of self-compassion and acceptance. You might silently say to yourself, "In this moment, I choose to treat myself with kindness and care." Or "I am worthy of love and respect, just as I am." Let these words resonate through your body and mind.

4. Gently begin to explore different forms of soothing self-touch. You might start by wrapping your arms around yourself in a nurturing self-embrace as if you were hugging a beloved friend. Feel the warmth and pressure of your touch and the comforting rhythm of your breath.

5. You can also experiment with offering yourself gentle strokes or caresses, perhaps along your arms, face, or torso. Let your touch be slow, tender, and attentive as if you were conveying a message of care and appreciation to your body.

6. Another option is to rest one or both hands over your heart center, feeling the steady beat of your heart beneath your palm. This gesture can be deeply calming and centering, as it reconnects you with your own life force and inner wisdom.

7. As you engage in self-touch, allow your movements to be organic and intuitive. Trust the wisdom of

your body to guide you toward the type of contact that feels most nourishing and supportive in the moment.

8. Throughout the practice, you can silently repeat affirmations or phrases of self-compassion, such as "I am here for you" or "I accept and love you, just as you are." Let these words infuse your touch with an added layer of intention and care.

9. Remember to keep breathing fully and deeply, imagining that your breath is flowing into and through the areas you are touching. If you encounter any resistance or discomfort, meet those sensations with patience and understanding, knowing that it takes time to develop new habits of self-relating.

Closing

As you complete this practice, take a moment to rest in the afterglow of your loving attention. Notice any shifts in your internal landscape, perhaps a greater sense of wholeness, tenderness, or self-acceptance. Consider integrating compassionate self-touch into your daily self-care routine, either as a standalone practice or as a complement to other forms of self-inquiry and healing. Over time, you may find that your capacity for self-love, self-forgiveness, and self-attunement naturally deepens and expands. Remember, the path of self-compassion is a lifelong journey, one that invites us to keep showing up for ourselves with presence, patience, and care. With each loving touch, you are planting seeds of self-worth and self-healing that will blossom in every area of your life.

EXERCISE: WRITING A LETTER TO YOUR BODY

Writing a letter to your body is a powerful practice for cultivating gratitude, attunement, and compassion for your physical self. By putting your feelings into words, you create an opportunity for deep reflection and dialogue with your somatic experience. This practice can be particularly transformative for those who struggle with body shame, disconnection, or neglect, as it opens a channel for rebuilding trust and rapport with the body. As you write, you may uncover new insights, heal old wounds, and develop a more loving, respectful relationship with your embodied being.

Guided Instructions

1. Begin by finding a comfortable, private space where you can write without interruption. Choose a location that feels safe and conducive to self-reflection, such as a cozy corner of your home or a quiet spot in nature. Gather your writing materials, whether a journal and pen or a computer.

2. Take a few slow, grounding breaths, allowing your awareness to turn inward. Close your eyes and notice the sensations of your body contacting the surface beneath you, the temperature of the air on your skin, and the gentle flow of your breath.

3. Now, guide your attention through a gradual body scan, starting at the crown of your head and moving down to the soles of your feet. As you attune to each region of your body, send a message of

acknowledgment and care. You might silently say, "I'm here with you. I'm listening."

4. As you tune into the different areas of your body, allow any images, metaphors, or feeling states to arise. You might notice a sense of tension or holding in certain places or a feeling of ease and vitality in others. Simply observe what emerges without judgment.

5. When you feel ready, begin free writing a stream-of-consciousness letter to your body. You can address your body as a whole or speak directly to specific parts or regions. Let your words flow freely without censoring or editing yourself.

6. As you write, express your appreciation for all the ways your body supports you and allows you to experience life. You might thank your legs for carrying you from place to place, your hands for allowing you to touch and create, or your heart for beating steadily day after day.

7. You can also acknowledge any challenges, pain, or difficulties your body has faced and express your compassion and understanding. You might say, "I know you've been through so much. I'm sorry for the times I've neglected or mistreated you. I'm here for you now."

8. Throughout the writing process, try to avoid self-judgment or criticism. Instead, lean into vulnerability, tenderness, and curiosity. Imagine that you are speaking to your body as you would a beloved friend or child, with patience and care.

9. When you feel complete, take a moment to read over your letter. Notice any insights, emotions, or shifts in perspective that have emerged. If it feels authentic, you might choose to speak certain parts of your letter aloud, as if in direct communion with your body.

Closing

As you complete this practice, take a moment to rest in the afterglow of your compassionate attention. Notice any shifts in your relationship with your body, perhaps a greater sense of intimacy, respect, or unity. Consider making this self-reflective writing a regular part of your self-care routine, whether through ongoing journaling or periodic letters. Over time, you may find that the simple act of putting your somatic experience into words can catalyze profound changes in how you inhabit and relate to your physical self. Remember, your body is always listening, always responding to the messages you send it. By engaging in this practice with honesty, humility, and love, you plant the seeds for a lifetime of embodied healing, vitality, and wholeness.

EXERCISE: SELF-COMPASSION BREAK

The Self-Compassion Break is a practical and empowering exercise that can be used in the midst of difficult situations to bring mindful awareness, a sense of common humanity, and self-kindness to one's experience. This practice, developed by Dr. Kristin Neff, helps to cultivate self-compassion as an inner resource that can be readily accessed in moments of pain, struggle, or overwhelm.

Steps

1. Think of a situation in your life that is causing you stress, suffering, or difficult emotions. It could be a current challenge, a past event that still troubles you, or a future worry. Choose a situation that is moderately difficult, not overwhelmingly painful.

2. Bring the situation to mind, and see if you can actually feel the stress and emotional discomfort in your body. Locate where you feel it the most.

3. Now, say to yourself:

- "This is a moment of suffering"

That's mindfulness. Other options include:

- "This hurts."
- "Ouch."
- "This is stress."

4. Then say to yourself:

- "Suffering is a part of life"

That's common humanity. Other options include:

- "I'm not alone. Others feel this way."
- "We all struggle in our lives."

5. Now, put your hands over your heart, feel the warmth of your hands and the gentle touch on your chest. Say to yourself:

- "May I be kind to myself"

You can also ask yourself, "What do I need to hear right now to express kindness to myself?" Is there a phrase that speaks to you in your particular situation, such as:

- "May I be patient."
- "May I give myself the compassion that I need."
- "May I learn to accept myself as I am."

- "May I forgive myself."
- "May I be strong."

6. If you're having difficulty finding the right words, imagine that a dear friend or loved one is having the same problem. What would you say to this person? If your friend would have an easier time being kind to you, put those words into your own mouth.

7. Take a few deep breaths, and rest in the feelings of self-compassion, self-care, and self-acceptance that arise. Know that you can return to these phrases and this practice whenever you need to.

Conclusion

The Self-Compassion Break is a transformative practice that can help you bring mindfulness, common humanity, and self-kindness to moments of pain or difficulty. By acknowledging suffering as a shared human experience and offering ourselves the compassion we would readily extend to a friend, we can start to soften the harsh, isolating edge of self-criticism and instead cultivate an inner ally of wisdom and support.

As you integrate this practice into your life, you may find that self-compassion becomes more automatically accessible in times of need, allowing you to navigate challenges with greater resilience, equanimity, and grace. Remember, self-compassion is a courageous act of emotional strength and wisdom, not a sign of weakness or self-pity. As you offer yourself care and understanding in difficult times, you enhance your capacity to be present with all of life's experiences, and to extend that same compassion to the wider world.

EXERCISE: COMPASSIONATE LETTER TO THE SELF

Writing a Compassionate Letter to the Self is a profound practice that invites you to direct the energy of compassion, understanding, and encouragement towards yourself, especially in the face of personal difficulties, failings, or aspects of yourself that you often criticize. By writing to yourself from the perspective of a kind, understanding friend, you can begin to internalize a more supportive and accepting inner voice, and to relate to yourself with greater warmth, care, and self-compassion.

Steps

1. Begin by finding a quiet, comfortable place where you can write without interruption. Have a pen and paper, or a computer if you prefer to type.

2. Take a few deep breaths, and bring to mind a current difficulty in your life, or an aspect of yourself that you often judge or criticize. This could be a perceived failure, a personal struggle, a physical feature, or a part of your personality that you find challenging to accept.

3. Now, imagine that a dear friend or loved one whom you deeply trust and respect is having this same difficulty or self-judgment. Picture them sitting with you, sharing their struggles openly and vulnerably.

4. Reflect on what you would say to this friend to offer them support, understanding, and encouragement. What words of kindness, care, and wisdom would you share? How might you remind them of their inherent worthiness, goodness, and human imperfection?

5. Begin to write a letter to yourself from the perspective of this compassionate friend. Address yourself by name, and express your empathy and understanding for the difficulty you are facing. Validate your emotions and experiences, without minimizing them or trying to fix them.

6. In the letter, remind yourself of your positive qualities, strengths, and capacities. Share specific examples of times when you have overcome challenges, shown resilience, or made a positive difference in your own or others' lives.

7. Offer yourself words of encouragement, support, and guidance, as if you were speaking to a dear friend. Remind yourself that struggles and imperfections are a part of the shared human experience, and that they do not diminish your worth or lovability.

8. As you write, if you encounter any blocks or resistance, take a deep breath and reconnect with the intention of compassion. If it feels difficult to write from a place of self-kindness, imagine what a truly loving friend or mentor would say to you in this situation.

9. When you feel you have fully expressed your compassionate message to yourself, sign the letter with a term of endearment or self-care, such as "With love and understanding, [Your Name]" or "Always in your corner, [Your Name]."

10. Take a moment to read the letter back to yourself, slowly and with feeling. Notice any emotions, sensations, or insights that arise. Allow the words of compassion to sink deeply into your heart and being.

11. If desired, you can keep this letter in a special place, and return to it whenever you need a reminder of your inherent worthiness and the power of self-compassion. You might also consider writing compassionate letters to yourself as a regular practice, addressing different aspects of your experience over time.

Conclusion

Writing a Compassionate Letter to the Self is a transformative practice that can help to shift the inner landscape from one of self-criticism and judgment to one of self-acceptance, care, and support. By intentionally generating the voice of a compassionate friend and directing it towards our own difficulties and imperfections, we begin to internalize a more accepting and encouraging inner dialogue.

As we practice this kind of self-compassionate communication, we may find that we are better able to navigate life's challenges with greater resilience, wisdom, and emotional balance. We may also discover a deeper sense of connection and common humanity, recognizing that our struggles and flaws do not isolate us, but in fact unite us with all beings.

18. THE ROLE OF CREATIVITY AND PLAY

In the realm of somatic healing, we often focus on the more serious and weighty aspects of the journey—the deep emotional processing, the challenging trauma work, and the slow and steady cultivation of new patterns and habits. While these elements are essential to the process of embodied transformation, another crucial ingredient is sometimes overlooked: the power of creativity and play.

At its core, creativity is about tapping into our innate capacity for imagination, curiosity, and spontaneity. It is about allowing ourselves to explore new possibilities, express ourselves in unique and authentic ways, and find joy and delight in the simple act of creation. When we engage in creative activities, whether through art, music, dance, or any other form of self-expression, we activate different neural networks in our brains and bodies, shifting us out of our habitual patterns and into a state of open-ended exploration.

THE IMPORTANCE OF CREATIVITY IN SOMATIC HEALING

From a somatic perspective, creativity and play serve several essential functions in the healing process. Primarily, they help to regulate our nervous system, moving us out of states of hyperarousal or hypo arousal and into a more balanced and integrated state of being. When we are stuck in patterns of chronic stress, trauma, or overwhelm, our bodies can become rigid and constricted, locked into a narrow range of responses and behaviors. But when we engage in creative play, we send a signal to our nervous system that it is safe to relax, let go of our defenses, and explore new possibilities.

This open-ended exploration is crucial for the rewiring of our neural pathways and the development of new patterns and habits. When we allow ourselves to play and experiment without judgment or expectation, we create space for new connections to form in our brains and bodies, laying the groundwork for lasting change and transformation. We also tap into our innate capacity for neuroplasticity—the ability of our brains to adapt and change in response to new experiences and information.

Another important function of creativity in somatic healing is its ability to facilitate symbolic inner working. When we engage in creative expression, we can access and express parts of ourselves that may be difficult to articulate through words alone. We can explore the deeper layers of our psyche, bringing unconscious material into conscious awareness and integrating it into our sense of self.

This symbolic inner working can be especially powerful for those who have experienced trauma or other forms of emotional wounding. Often, the experiences that have caused us the greatest pain and suffering are the ones that are the most difficult to talk about or even think about directly. But through creative expression, we can find ways to indirectly engage with these experiences, tell our stories in new and healing ways, and find meaning and purpose in even the darkest of times.

Suggestions for Inspiring Creative Somatic Activities

If you are new to the idea of incorporating creativity and play into your somatic healing journey, here are a few suggestions to get you started:

1. Free-form dance: Put on some music that moves you and allows your body to express itself freely, without judgment or expectation. Notice how it feels to let go of your habitual patterns and surrender to the rhythm and flow of the music.

2. Intuitive artmaking: Gather some art supplies (paper, markers, paints, etc.) and set aside some time to create without any specific goal or outcome in mind. Allow yourself to be guided by your intuition and inner sense of knowing, trusting that whatever emerges is exactly what needs to be expressed at that moment.

3. Improvisational theater games: Engage in simple improv games with friends or family members, such as "Yes, and..." or "Word at a Time Story." Notice how it feels to let go of your need for control and perfection and embrace the spontaneity and creativity of the moment.

4. Nature play: Spend time in nature, allowing yourself to explore and interact with your surroundings in a childlike way. Climb a tree, splash in a puddle, or lie in the grass and watch the clouds drift by. Notice how it feels to reconnect with your sense of wonder and awe.

5. Somatic poetry: Write a poem or short piece of prose about your embodied experience in the moment. Focus on the sensations, emotions, and images that arise without worrying about whether they make sense or sound "good." Allow the words to flow freely from your body onto the page.

Remember, the goal of these activities is not to create a masterpiece or impress others with your artistic talents. Rather, it is to tap into your innate capacity for creativity and play, shift your nervous system into a more regulated and resourced state, and explore new possibilities for healing and growth.

As you begin to incorporate more creativity and play into your somatic healing journey, you may find that it becomes an essential part of your self-care routine. You may discover new aspects of yourself that you never knew existed and find joy and delight in even the most mundane moments. You may also find that your capacity for resilience and adaptability increases as you become more skilled at navigating life's difficulties with a sense of curiosity and open heartedness.

EXERCISE: EXPRESSIVE ARTS FOR EMBODIMENT

Expressive arts, such as painting, drawing, sculpting, and free-form movement, can provide powerful avenues for somatic exploration and integration. By engaging in the creative process, we open a direct channel to the body's innate wisdom, allowing our inner experiences to find shape and form. This practice is an invitation to step out of the cognitive realm and into the body's intuitive voice. It does not require any technical skills or artistic training, only a willingness to let go of expectations and immerse oneself in the sensory, kinesthetic experience of creation.

Guided Instructions

1. Begin by preparing a creative space with a variety of art supplies and materials. This might include paper, paints, markers, clay, fabric, or any other mediums that call to you. You can also incorporate elements for sound-making, such as simple instruments or everyday objects. Ensure that you have ample room to move and make a mess.

2. Take a few slow, grounding breaths, allowing your awareness to settle into your body. Notice any sensations, emotions, or impulses that are present without judgment or interpretation. Attune to your inner landscape with open, curious attention.

3. When you feel ready, allow your body to guide you towards a particular material or modality. You might feel drawn to the rich, tactile sensation of fingerpaint, the fluid motion of dancing with streamers, or the primal energy of pounding on a drum. Trust your instincts and follow your somatic cues.

4. As you engage with your chosen medium, give yourself full permission to explore and experiment. Rather than trying to create a specific image or outcome, let your expression evolve organically, guided by your bodily sensations and impulses. You might make bold, sweeping gestures with your arms or slow, swirling patterns with your fingertips.

5. Throughout the process, stay anchored in your felt experience. Notice the textures, temperatures, and movements of your body as it interacts with the materials. If you find yourself getting caught up in mental analysis or self-judgment, gently redirect your attention back to the sensory realm.

6. Feel free to incorporate different mediums and modalities fluidly, as your body desires. You might alternate between painting and dancing or between sculpting and vocalizing. Allow yourself to be surprised and delighted by the unexpected synergies that emerge.

7. At times, you might find yourself naturally shifting into a more receptive, witnessing state. In these moments, observe your creation with soft, appreciative attention. Notice what it evokes in your body without the need to interpret or assign meaning.

8. As your exploration begins to naturally wind down, take a few moments to rest in stillness, savoring the afterglow of your creative expression. Notice any shifts in your bodily sensations, energy levels, or emotional state. You might feel a sense of release, integration, or newfound clarity.

Closing

As you complete this practice, take a moment to appreciate your body's innate capacity for creative expression and self-discovery. Honor the courage and vulnerability it takes to step into the unknown and trust the wisdom of your somatic impulses. Consider integrating expressive arts into your regular self-care routine to continually deepen your relationship with your embodied self. Over time, you may find that this type of free-form creation becomes a powerful tool for processing emotions, releasing blocked energy, and accessing new levels of insight and integration. Remember, your body is always speaking, always creating, always offering its raw materials for healing and transformation. By engaging in expressive arts with openness, curiosity, and reverence, you honor the richness and resilience of your embodied experience.

EXERCISE: PLAYFUL MOVEMENT GAMES

Playful movement games are a wonderful way to unlock joy, spontaneity, and embodied presence. By engaging in these activities, we give ourselves permission to step out of habitual patterns and explore new ways of being in our bodies. These games are not about performance or skill but rather about cultivating a sense of curiosity, wonder, and aliveness. They invite us to rediscover the inherent pleasure and creativity of movement and to connect with others in a spirit of mutual attunement and discovery.

Guided Instructions

1. Mirroring:

- In pairs, take turns embodying different movements and postures, which your partner then mirrors back to you. Start with slow, simple gestures and gradually build in complexity and speed.
- As you mirror each other, pay attention to the subtle nuances of your partner's movements, as well as your bodily sensations and impulses. Notice how it feels to lead and follow, to attune and respond.

2. Sculpting:

- In pairs, take turns gently sculpting each other's bodies into different forms and shapes. You can use your hands to guide your partner's limbs, torso, and head into various configurations.
- As the sculptor, bring a sense of care and reverence to your touch, honoring your partner's boundaries and comfort level. As the sculpture, allow yourself to be molded and shaped, trusting in the safety of the container.

3. Animal Flows:

- As a group, take turns exploring movements inspired by different creatures, such as snakes, birds, cats, or elephants. Encourage each other to fully embody the qualities and characteristics of each animal.

- Allow your movements to be guided by your felt sense of the animal, rather than by mental concepts or stereotypes. Notice how your body naturally wants to express the essence of each creature.

4. Authentic Movement Jam:

- In a group, create a designated space for free-form movement exploration. Without any discussion or planning, allow yourselves to intuitively move together, responding to each other's energy and impulses.
- Let your movements be guided by your inner sensations, emotions, and imagery, rather than by external cues or expectations. Trust in the wisdom of your body to express itself authentically in each moment.

For each of these activities, emphasize the spirit of experimentation, play, and beginner's mind. Encourage participants to let go of self-judgment and perfectionism and to embrace the messy, unpolished beauty of spontaneous expression. Invite elements of humor, silliness, and lightheartedness, remembering that laughter is a powerful form of somatic release and connection.

Closing

As you complete these playful movement games, take a moment to savor the aliveness and vitality that you have generated. Notice any shifts in your energy level, emotional state, or sense of embodiment. Consider integrating these types of activities into your regular movement practice to continually refresh your relationship with your body and with others. Remember, play is a vital nutrient for our somatic and relational well-being. By engaging in these games with an open heart and a curious spirit, we reconnect with the joy, creativity, and resilience that are our birthright. May you carry this sense of embodied play into all areas of your life, and may it nourish you on your ongoing journey of growth and self-discovery.

EXERCISE: CREATING A SOMATIC HEALING MANDALA

Mandalas are circular designs that have been used for centuries to represent wholeness, integration, and the cyclical nature of life. In this practice, we will be creating a mandala as an embodied, intuitive expression of your inner somatic landscape. This is an opportunity to let your body's wisdom guide the creative process, allowing shapes, colors, and symbols to emerge organically from your felt sense. There are no rules or expectations in this practice, only an invitation to explore, discover, and give form to your embodied experience.

Guided Instructions

1. Begin by gathering your art supplies, such as paper, pens, pencils, markers, crayons, or paints. Choose materials that feel inviting and accessible to you and that allow for a range of expressive possibilities.

2. Find a quiet, comfortable space where you can work on your mandala without interruption. You might choose to play soft instrumental music or enjoy the natural sounds of your environment. Ensure that you have ample room to spread out your supplies and move freely.

3. Take a few slow, ground breaths, allowing your awareness to settle into your body. Notice any sensations, emotions, or energetic qualities that are present without judgment or interpretation. Attune to your inner landscape with open, curious attention.

4. When you feel ready, begin by drawing a simple circle in the center of your paper. This circle represents the core of your being, the still point from which your somatic experience unfolds. You can use a compass, trace a round object, or freehand your circle.

5. Allow your body's intuitive wisdom to guide your hand as you begin to add shapes, lines, and colors to your mandala. Let these elements emerge organically from the center, radiating outward in whatever way feels natural and authentic to you.

6. As you create, stay connected to your somatic awareness. Notice how each color, texture, and form resonates in your body. You might choose hues that evoke a particular feeling state or shapes that capture a physical sensation. Trust your instincts and let your body lead the way.

7. Work slowly and mindfully, adding layers and details as your mandala evolves. You might find yourself drawn to repeating patterns, symmetrical designs, or abstract expressions. Allow yourself to be surprised and delighted by the unique creation that emerges.

8. If you encounter any moments of creative block or self-doubt, take a pause, and reconnect with your breath. Remind yourself that there is no right or wrong way to create your mandala and that every mark you make is an authentic expression of your embodied self.

9. As your mandala feels complete, take a step back and witness your creation with soft, appreciative eyes. Notice what it evokes in your body and any insights or reflections that arise. You might journal about your experience or sit in quiet contemplation.

Closing

As you complete this practice, honor the wisdom and creativity of your embodied self. Your mandala is a sacred reflection of your inner world, a tangible expression of your somatic story. Consider displaying your mandala in a place where you'll see it regularly as a reminder of your body's innate capacity for healing, integration, and self-expression. You might also choose to create mandalas on a regular basis to track your somatic journey over time. Remember, your body is always speaking, always creating, always offering its raw materials for transformation. By engaging in this practice with presence, openness, and reverence, you honor the deep intelligence and resilience of your embodied being.

19. DESIGNING YOUR PERSONALIZED SOMATIC PRACTICE

As we near the end of our exploration of somatic healing, it is important to consider how we can integrate the insights, practices, and tools we have learned into our daily lives in a sustainable and nourishing way. While profound experiences in workshops, retreats, or therapy sessions can be transformative at the moment, it is the daily practice of embodied presence and self-care that truly allows these changes to take root and flourish over time.

Designing a personalized somatic practice is an essential part of any embodied healing journey. It is a way of creating a sacred space in your life for self-inquiry, self-discovery, and self-transformation. In this space, you can regularly tune in to the wisdom of your body, mind, and spirit and cultivate the skills and capacities that will support you in navigating life's ups and downs with greater ease, resilience, and grace.

THE BENEFITS OF DAILY PRACTICE

One of the most powerful benefits of daily somatic practice is the way it allows for deep experiential learning over time. When we engage in embodied practices consistently, we create the conditions for new neural pathways to form and strengthen, gradually rewiring our brains and bodies for greater presence, awareness, and regulation.

This experiential learning is different from intellectual understanding; it is grounded in the felt sense of our own embodied experience and becomes deeply integrated into our very being over time. Through daily practice, we begin to install the neural traits of embodied presence as our default mode of being, becoming more skilled at noticing and interrupting patterns of reactivity, dissociation, or overwhelm and cultivating states of grounded, centered, and open-hearted awareness. We also develop a greater capacity for self-compassion, self-care, and self-regulation, learning to attune to and respond to our bodies' needs and signals with greater sensitivity and skill.

The benefits of daily practice are not necessarily dependent on the length or intensity of each session; research has shown that consistency and frequency of practice are most important for creating lasting change. Even a few minutes of embodied practice each day can have a profound impact over time, as the cumulative effects of these small moments of presence and self-care add up.

Many somatic practitioners recommend a "little and often" approach to daily practice, integrating short moments of embodied awareness and self-care throughout the day rather than trying to carve out large chunks of time for intensive practice sessions. By weaving these small moments of practice into the fabric of daily life, you create an embodied safety net that can support you in navigating the inevitable stresses and challenges of modern living while developing a more intimate and trusting relationship with your own body and mind.

EXERCISE: CRAFTING YOUR SOMATIC RITUAL

Rituals are powerful tools for anchoring us in embodied presence and creating a sense of sacred space in our daily lives. By intentionally designing a personalized somatic ritual, we can weave together the practices and elements that most resonate with our unique needs and desires. This is an opportunity to craft a consistent, nourishing container for your ongoing somatic exploration and growth. The act of ritualizing our practice supports deeper integration, commitment, and transformation over time.

Guided Instructions

1. Begin by reflecting on the various somatic techniques and practices that you've explored in your journey thus far. Consider which ones have resonated most deeply with your body and being and have offered you a felt sense of grounding, ease, or aliveness.

2. Contemplate what types of transitional cues or elements could help shift your state and signal to your body that you're entering a sacred space of practice. This might include certain types of music, lighting, scents, or objects that hold personal significance for you.

- Examples: Soft, instrumental music; dimmed, candlelit ambiance; essential oils or incense; a special cushion, blanket, or altar cloth.

3. Begin to sketch out a general sequence or flow that feels organic and nourishing for your body. Consider how you might like to move through different stages of your practice, such as breathwork, movement, stillness, and reflection.

- Examples: Starting with grounding breaths, flowing into gentle stretches, moving into free-form dance, settling into silent meditation, and closing with journaling or self-massage.

4. Explore how you might create a sense of embodied opening and closing to your ritual to mark the boundaries of your sacred space. This could be a simple gesture, such as placing your hands on your heart, or a more elaborate sequence, such as lighting a candle or ringing a bell.

5. Determine the ideal timing, location, and duration for your somatic ritual. Consider when you feel most energized and available and where you have access to a quiet, private space. Aim for a length of practice that feels sustainable and nourishing rather than depleting.

6. As you design your ritual, allow it to carry personal meaning and symbolism. You might choose to include elements that reflect your cultural heritage, spiritual beliefs, or natural environment. Let your creativity and intuition guide you in crafting a ritual that feels authentic and resonant.

7. Remember that your somatic ritual is a flexible, evolving container, not a rigid prescription. Approach it with a sense of openness, curiosity, and self-compassion, and allow it to change and grow

alongside you. Trust that your body will guide you towards the practices and elements that most serve your healing and wholeness.

Closing

As you complete the design of your somatic ritual, take a moment to honor your commitment to your own embodied well-being. By crafting a personalized practice that reflects your unique needs and desires, you are claiming your inherent right to safety, nourishment, and self-care. Consider sharing your ritual with a trusted friend, therapist, or community to deepen your accountability and support. Remember, your somatic ritual is a living, breathing expression of your ever-unfolding relationship with your body and inner world. By engaging with it consistently and reverently, you are planting seeds of transformation that will blossom in every area of your life. May your ritual be a source of grounding, healing, and revelation on your ongoing journey of embodied awakening.

OVERCOMING OBSTACLES TO PRACTICE

Maintaining a consistent daily practice can be challenging at times, even with the best of intentions. Common pitfalls that can derail our practice include lack of time or energy, resistance or avoidance, perfectionism or self-judgment, and lack of support or accountability.

To overcome these obstacles and realign with our commitment to daily practice, we can employ various strategies and tools, such as:

- Reevaluating priorities and consciously choosing to prioritize practice as an essential part of self-care and well-being.
- Breaking practice into smaller, more manageable chunks that can be easily integrated into daily routines.
- Cultivating an attitude of curiosity, compassion, and non-judgment toward whatever arises in practice.
- Seeking support and accountability from a community of like-minded practitioners or a trusted teacher or mentor.
- Being willing to adapt and modify practice over time to better suit changing needs, circumstances, and lifestyle.

The key to sustaining a nourishing daily practice is approaching it with a spirit of curiosity, experimentation, and self-compassion, finding practices and routines that work best for you, and being willing to adjust and adapt as needed over time. This may involve experimenting with different times of day, modalities, and techniques, starting small and building up gradually, and being gentle and forgiving with yourself when you inevitably fall off track, remembering that each moment is a new opportunity to begin again.

As you design your personalized somatic practice, start by reflecting on your unique needs, goals, and values. Consider areas of life where you feel most in need of support, nourishment, or growth, practices, or modalities you have found most helpful or inspiring in the past, and times of day or settings where you feel most grounded, present, and resourced.

From there, sketch out a rough outline of your daily practice, keeping in mind the principles of consistency, flexibility, and self-compassion. Choose to anchor your practice around a particular time of day, focus on a specific modality or set of practices, and set intentions or goals for your practice, such as cultivating greater self-awareness, self-regulation, or self-compassion.

As you implement your daily practice, track your progress and experiences in a journal or log, noting insights, challenges, or breakthroughs that arise along the way. This can be a valuable tool for self-reflection and self-discovery, as well as a way of holding yourself accountable and celebrating your growth and progress over time.

EXERCISE: SOMATIC SELF-CARE MENU

Self-care is an essential practice for nourishing resilience, preventing burnout, and cultivating overall well-being. By creating a personalized menu of embodied self-care activities, we can ensure that we have a diverse range of nourishing practices to draw upon, no matter what our energy level or time availability. The key is to tailor our self-care menu to our unique needs and preferences and to choose practices that are realistically sustainable in our daily lives. With a well-stocked self-care toolkit, we can more easily navigate the inevitable ups and downs of our somatic journey.

Guided Instructions

1. Begin by reflecting on the somatic self-care activities that you currently enjoy and find replenishing. This might include practices such as yoga, dance, meditation, massage, or taking a warm bath. Consider what helps you feel grounded, energized, or at ease in your body.

2. Next, browse through the various practices and exercises in this workbook and identify any that you'd like to explore further. Perhaps you're drawn to the idea of expressive arts, or you'd like to experiment with breathwork or mindful movement. Trust your intuition and let your body guide you towards what feels most nourishing.

3. As you gather your self-care ideas, begin to categorize them by the amount of time they require. Create separate lists for practices that take 5 minutes or less (such as deep breathing or affirmations), 10-30 minutes (such as meditation or gentle stretching), and 1 hour or more (such as a somatic therapy session or nature immersion).

4. Once you have your categorized lists, consider creating a visually appealing self-care menu that you can display in your home or carry with you. You might design a colorful poster, a digital graphic, or a small booklet that showcases your personalized self-care options.

5. As you finalize your self-care menu, take some time to reflect on when and how frequently you'd like to engage in each practice. Consider scheduling regular self-care time into your calendar and setting realistic goals for how often you'll engage in different types of activities.

6. Identify any materials, spaces, or support you might need to enable your self-care practices. This could include things like a yoga mat, art supplies, a dedicated meditation corner, or a therapy appointment. Take steps to gather these resources and create a supportive environment for your self-care.

7. Remember that your self-care menu is a living document, not a fixed prescription. Allow it to evolve and expand as you discover new practices and rediscover your body's changing needs. Approach your self-care with a spirit of curiosity, experimentation, and self-compassion, and trust that even the smallest acts of nourishment can have a ripple effect on your overall well-being.

Closing

As you complete your somatic self-care menu, take a moment to appreciate your commitment to your own embodied well-being. By intentionally crafting a diverse range of nourishing practices, you are claiming your inherent worthiness of care and attention. Consider sharing your self-care menu with a trusted friend or loved one to build accountability and support. Remember, self-care is not a luxury or a selfish indulgence but a vital necessity for navigating the complexities of human experience. By tending to your body's needs with consistency and compassion, you are laying the foundation for greater resilience, vitality, and joy in all areas of your life. May your self-care menu be a source of nourishment, grounding, and renewal on your ongoing journey of embodied transformation.

20. EMBODYING YOUR RESILIENCE

As we come to the close of our exploration of somatic healing, it is important to reflect on the incredible journey we have undertaken together. Throughout these pages, we have delved into the depths of our embodied experience, exploring the ways in which our bodies hold and express the stories of our lives. We have learned about the profound impact of stress, trauma, and adversity on our physical, emotional, and relational well-being, as well as the many pathways to healing and transformation that are available to us through somatic practice.

At the heart of this journey, we have discovered the innate resilience and intelligence of our own embodied being. We have come to understand that no matter how lost, disconnected, or overwhelmed we may feel at times, there is always a part of us that is whole, intact, and capable of growth and change. This is the essence of resilience—the capacity to adapt, recover, and thrive in the face of adversity, drawing on the deep wells of strength, wisdom, and compassion that live within us.

WHAT IS RESILIENCE?

In psychology, resilience is often defined as the ability to bounce back from difficult experiences, adapt, and grow in the face of stress and adversity. It is the capacity to not only survive but also thrive, even in the most challenging circumstances.

From a somatic perspective, resilience is deeply rooted in the body's innate capacity for self-regulation and healing. When we experience stress or trauma, our nervous system is thrown out of balance, activating a cascade of physiological responses designed to help us survive the perceived threat. While these responses can be adaptive in the short term, they can also take a toll on our bodies and minds over time if our nervous system gets stuck in a state of chronic activation or shutdown.

The key to building resilience, then, is not to avoid or suppress these stress responses altogether but rather to develop the capacity to move through them with greater ease, flexibility, and self-awareness. This is where somatic practices come in—by helping us cultivate a deeper and more nuanced relationship with our own embodied experience, we can learn to regulate our nervous system, release chronic tension and holding patterns, and adapt more skillfully to the challenges and opportunities of our lives.

HOW SOMATIC PRACTICES BUILD EMBODIED RESILIENCE

Throughout this book, we have explored a wide range of somatic practices designed to support resilience and well-being, from grounding and centering techniques to breath awareness, mindful movement, and self-compassion. Each of these practices, in its own way, helps to build the physiological and emotional flexibility that underlies true resilience.

For example, grounding and centering practices help us anchor ourselves in the present moment, cultivating a sense of stability and safety in the body. Breath awareness and regulation allow us to use the power of our breath to shift our physiological state in real time, counteracting the effects of chronic stress and anxiety. Mindful movement practices, such as yoga, tai chi, or qigong, help release chronic tension, improve posture and alignment, and cultivate a greater sense of ease and flow in our daily lives.

Perhaps most importantly, somatic practices help to cultivate the inner resources of self-awareness, self-compassion, and self-care that are so essential for resilience. When we learn to tune into the subtle cues and signals of our body, we develop a greater capacity to respond to our own needs with kindness, curiosity, and care, treating ourselves with the same level of respect, understanding, and support that we would offer to a dear friend or loved one.

SUSTAINING YOUR JOURNEY

As you continue your journey of embodied resilience, remember that this is a lifelong process that requires ongoing commitment, practice, and support. There will be times when you feel strong, centered, and capable, and other times when you feel vulnerable, overwhelmed, or lost. This is all part of the natural ebb and flow of the human experience, and it is okay to honor and embrace the full range of your emotions and sensations.

One key to sustaining your practice is to cultivate an attitude of self-compassion and celebration along the way. Take time to acknowledge and appreciate the progress you have made, no matter how small or incremental it may seem. Recognize that every moment of awareness, every breath, every movement is an opportunity to deepen your relationship with yourself and your own embodied experience.

It can also be helpful to have a range of strategies and practices to draw upon when you feel stuck, confused, or disconnected, such as reaching out to a trusted friend, therapist, or teacher for support or engaging in a favorite somatic practice that helps you feel grounded, centered, and resourced. Setting intentions or goals for your practice and breaking them down into small, manageable steps can also be beneficial.

My deepest wish for you, as you continue your path of embodied resilience, is that you may always remember the innate wisdom, beauty, and strength that resides within you. May you trust in the intelligence of your own body, mind, and spirit, and may you have the courage to listen to and honor their guidance. May you surround yourself with people, practices, and environments that nourish and support your ongoing growth and development. May you always know that no matter what challenges or obstacles you may face, you have everything you need within you to adapt, thrive, and flourish.

Thank you from the bottom of my heart for the privilege of sharing this journey with you. May your path be filled with love, laughter, and endless opportunities for growth and transformation. May you always remember that you are resilient, capable, and worthy of the life you desire.

EXERCISE: IDENTIFYING YOUR STRENGTHS AND RESOURCES

Focusing on our inner resources and strengths is a powerful way to build resilience and navigate life's challenges with greater ease and self-compassion. By taking inventory of the positive qualities, capacities, and skills that already reside within us, we cultivate a sense of self-empowerment and trust in our ability to handle whatever arises. This practice is an invitation to shift our attention from perceived deficits to the inherent wisdom, creativity, and resilience that we embody. The goal is to deepen our appreciation for the wholeness of our being and to draw upon our internal resources as a source of strength and support.

Guided Instructions

1. Begin by finding a calm, relaxed posture that allows you to reflect inwardly with ease. You might sit in a comfortable chair, with your feet planted on the ground and your spine long and dignified. Or you might stand with your feet hip-width apart, your knees slightly soft, and your shoulders relaxed.

2. Take a few slow, grounding breaths, allowing your body to settle and your mind to grow still. With each exhalation, imagine creating a spacious field of awareness within yourself, a vast open sky that can hold all your experiences with equanimity.

3. When you feel ready, guide your attention through a gentle body scan, starting at the crown of your head and moving down to the soles of your feet. As you traverse the various regions of your body, silently acknowledge the inherent wisdom, strength, and resilience that each part embodies.

4. As you complete your body scan, begin to reflect on the personality strengths and positive qualities that you possess. These might include traits such as resilience, compassion, curiosity, integrity, or adaptability. Make a mental or written list of the strengths that resonate most deeply with your sense of self.

- Examples: "I am resilient in the face of adversity," "I approach challenges with curiosity and openness," and "I lead with compassion and empathy."

5. Next, consider the various capacities, skills, and talents that you embody. These might include creative abilities, analytical skills, nurturing instincts, or leadership qualities. Again, make a mental or written list of the capacities that you value and appreciate in yourself.

- Examples: "I have a gift for creative problem-solving," "I am skilled at deep listening and empathy," and "I have a talent for bringing people together towards a common goal."

6. To integrate your reflections, consider creating a visual representation of your inner resources and

strengths. This might be a simple sketch or drawing of yourself surrounded by affirmative words or symbols. Or, it could be a more abstract portrait, using colors, shapes, and textures to evoke the qualities and capacities you've identified.

7. As you complete your visual representation, take a moment to voice your self-appreciation and gratitude aloud. You might say something like, "I honor the strength and resilience that I embody," or "I am grateful for the gifts and talents that I bring to the world." Allow yourself to fully receive and absorb these affirmations.

8. If you feel called, consider sharing your reflective process with a trusted friend, family member, or therapist. Inviting others to witness and celebrate your strengths and resources can deepen your sense of appreciation and empowerment.

Closing

As you complete this practice, take a moment to rest in the spaciousness and abundance of your inner landscape. Notice any shifts in your energy, perspective, or self-concept, and allow yourself to marinate in the felt sense of your inherent worthiness and sufficiency. Remember, your strengths and resources are not fixed or finite but ever evolving and expanding with each new experience and insight. By regularly attuning to and appreciating these inner assets, you build a foundation of self-trust and self-compassion that can support you through all of life's difficulties. May you carry this practice forward as a reminder of your innate wholeness, resilience, and capacity for growth and transformation.

EXERCISE: EMBODYING YOUR INNER HERO/INE

This practice is an invitation to connect with the heroic qualities that reside within each of us, such as courage, strength, determination, and resilience. By exploring and embodying these qualities through physical expression and imagination, we can access a deeper sense of our inner resources and potential. This is not about emulating external heroic figures but rather about celebrating the unique heroic nature that already exists within us. Through this practice, we can cultivate a more empowered and purposeful relationship with ourselves and the challenges we face.

Guided Instructions

1. Begin by finding an open, unobstructed space where you can move around freely. This might be a clear area in your home, a spacious room, or an outdoor setting. Ensure that you have enough room to extend your arms and legs fully and to move in any direction.

2. Take a few slow, grounding breaths, allowing your body to settle and your mind to grow still. As you breathe, guide your attention through a gentle body scan, noticing any areas of tension, discomfort, or vitality. Acknowledge these sensations without judgment and invite a sense of curiosity and openness.

3. When you feel ready, allow an image of a heroic figure to emerge from within your being. This might be a character from myth, literature, or popular culture, or it could be a unique creation of your own imagination. Notice the qualities and characteristics that define this figure, such as their posture, demeanor, and inner resolve.

4. Begin to give your inner hero/ine a chance to "come alive" through your own body. Explore different physical expressions, such as poses, gestures, and movements, which capture the essence of this figure. You might find yourself standing tall with your chest open and your gaze focused or moving with purposeful strides and determined footsteps.

5. As you embody your inner hero/ine, notice the qualities and sensations that arise within you. You might feel a sense of power, purpose, or unwavering commitment to your values and goals. Allow yourself to fully inhabit these qualities as if you are channeling the energy and spirit of your heroic self.

6. If it feels authentic and enlivening, consider giving voice to your inner hero/ine through motivating battle cries, self-affirmations, or declarations of intent. You might say something like, "I am strong, I am capable, I am resilient," or "I face challenges with courage and determination." Allow your voice to be a channel for the heroic qualities you are embodying.

7. As you continue to explore and embody your inner hero/ine, imagine this figure as a source of guidance and support in your current life challenges. What wisdom or encouragement might they offer you? How might they approach the obstacles or uncertainties you are facing? Allow their perspective and energy to infuse your sense of possibility and empowerment.

8. Remember to approach this practice with a spirit of playfulness, spontaneity, and self-compassion. There is no right or wrong way to embody your inner hero/ine, and the process may evolve and change each time you engage with it. Trust your instincts and creativity and allow yourself to be surprised and delighted by what emerges.

Closing

As you complete this practice, take a moment to honor and celebrate the heroic qualities that you have connected with and expressed. Notice any shifts in your energy, perspective, or sense of self, and allow yourself to integrate these insights into your daily life. Remember, your inner hero/ine is not a distant or unattainable ideal but a reflection of your inherent strength, courage, and resilience. By regularly attuning to and embodying these qualities, you can cultivate a more empowered and purposeful relationship with yourself and the world around you. May you carry this practice forward as a reminder of your heroic nature and as a source of inspiration and support in navigating life's challenges and opportunities.

EXERCISE: CULTIVATING SUPPORTIVE RELATIONSHIPS

Positive, supportive relationships are essential to our overall well-being and resilience. By surrounding ourselves with people who offer empathy, encouragement, and inspiration, we create a solid foundation for navigating life's challenges and opportunities. This practice is an invitation to explore what healthy support looks and feels like in your own life and to set intentions for strengthening existing connections and attracting new ones. The goal is to cultivate a nourishing relational ecosystem that can support you in your ongoing growth and healing.

Guided Instructions

1. Begin by finding a relaxed, comfortable posture that allows you to feel both alert and at ease. You might sit in a chair with your feet planted on the ground or stand with your feet hip-width apart and your knees slightly soft. Take a few slow, grounding breaths, allowing your body to settle and your mind to grow still.

2. Guide your awareness inward through a gentle body scan, starting at the crown of your head and moving down to the soles of your feet. As you traverse the various regions of your body, notice any sensations of tension, ease, or aliveness. Acknowledge these sensations without judgment and invite a sense of curiosity and openness.

3. When you feel settled and present, begin to call to mind the supportive individuals currently in your life. These might include friends, family members, mentors, or colleagues who offer you a sense of connection, understanding, and encouragement. Allow their faces and presence to arise in your mind's eye.

4. For each person who comes to mind, take a moment to reflect on the specific qualities that make them supportive. Perhaps they offer a nonjudgmental listening ear or provide wise guidance and perspective. Maybe they inspire you with their resilience and growth or make you laugh and feel more at ease. Make a mental note of these qualities.

- Examples: "My friend Sarah always offers empathy and validation," "My mentor John provides insightful guidance and encouragement," "My sister Amy makes me laugh and helps me keep things in perspective."

5. As you reflect on these supportive individuals, tune into the felt sense of your experiences with them. Notice any sensations of warmth, relaxation, or expansiveness in your body. Allow yourself to fully receive and savor the feeling of being truly seen, heard, and supported. Anchor this somatic resonance in your body.

6. Now, begin to envision your "dream team" of support in the future. In addition to the people already in your life, what other types of supportive connections would feel nourishing and important? Perhaps you desire a mentor in your field or a community of like-minded individuals pursuing similar goals. Allow your imagination to explore the possibilities.

7. As you complete this reflection, set a clear intention to nurture your current supportive relationships and to attract new ones that align with your values and needs. You might silently affirm, "I am open to receiving and generating supportive connections," or "I surround myself with people who inspire and uplift me." Feel the power of this intention resonating in your body.

Closing

As you complete this practice, please take a moment to appreciate the supportive relationships that already exist in your life and to feel excited about the new connections that are on their way. Remember, cultivating a thriving relational ecosystem is an ongoing process that requires intention, effort, and vulnerability. By regularly attuning to the qualities of healthy support and taking steps to nurture these connections, you create a powerful foundation for your resilience and flourishing. May you continue to surround yourself with people who celebrate your authenticity, champion your growth, and remind you of your inherent worthiness.

Congratulations on completing this somatic therapy workbook! You've taken an important step in reconnecting with your body's innate wisdom and learning to befriend the cognitive, emotional, and physical experiences that arise within you.

Through the somatic exercises and practices in this workbook, you've begun reintegrating mind and body, releasing long-held tensions and traumas, and developing self-awareness and self-regulation skills. This is no small feat. Undoing habitual patterns of disconnection and developing a more embodied presence takes tremendous courage and commitment.

As you move forward, remember that the journey of somatic therapy is a lifelong practice of coming home to yourself. There will be times when you feel highly attuned to your bodily sensations and others when you feel disconnected again. This ebb and flow is normal. The key is to keep returning to the body over and over with compassion and curiosity.

If you find this book helpful and could benefit others, please leave a review on Amazon. It would mean a word to me if you do so.

Best wishes,

Yevhenii

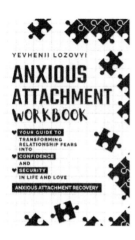

Anxious Attachment Workbook: Your Guide to Transforming Relationship Fears into Confidence and Security in Life and Love

Break free from the chains of anxious attachment with the "Anxious Attachment Workbook" - a powerful guide tailored to help you rewrite your love story. Through profound self-reflection exercises and insights into the roots of your attachment style, you'll embark on a transformative journey toward self-awareness and personal growth. Master communication techniques to foster openness and meet emotional needs, while cultivating radical self-love to boost confidence during relationship challenges. With actionable strategies for building secure, trusting bonds and preventing future heartache, this workbook equips you to transform fears into freedom. You'll find the tools to balance independence and intimacy, deepen emotional connections, and lay the foundation for lasting love and fulfillment.

Couples Therapy Workbook: Strategies to Connect, Restore Love and Trust, Improve Communication Intimacy and Validation

Reignite the spark in your relationship with the "Couples Therapy Workbook" - a comprehensive 7-week program designed to foster deeper emotional connection, conflict resolution skills, and lasting intimacy. Grounded in evidence-based techniques from renowned therapeutic approaches like the Gottman Method, Emotionally Focused Therapy, and Imago Relationship Therapy, this interactive workbook guides you and your partner through over 60 transformative exercises. Explore improved communication strategies, identify negative patterns, enhance emotional understanding, and rediscover appreciation and romance. With expert insights and activities promoting validation, trust, and carefree bonding, this all-encompassing guide provides the tools to overcome relationship obstacles and cultivate a future brimming with love and fulfillment.

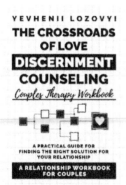

The Crossroads of Love: Discernment Counseling Couples Therapy Workbook a Practical Guide for Finding the Right Solution for Your Relationship

Are you in a relationship crossroads, unsure whether to pursue couples therapy, separate, or stay the course? "The Crossroads of Love" is an invaluable workbook for mixed-agenda couples struggling with indecision about their relationship's future. This comprehensive guide demystifies the discernment counseling process, providing evidence-based strategies and hands-on exercises to foster open communication, identify core issues, and navigate towards the path that's right for you both - whether that means reinvesting in the relationship through therapy, pursuing an amicable divorce, or achieving a newfound understanding to stay together.

REFERENCES

Aposhyan, S. M. (2004). Body-Mind Psychotherapy: Principles, Techniques, and Practical Applications. W. W. Norton.

Aposhyan, S. M. (2007). Natural Intelligence: Body-Mind Integration and Human Development. Now Press.

Bainbridge Cohen, B., Nelson, L., & Smith, N. S. (1993). Sensing, Feeling, and Action: The Experiential Anatomy of Body-Mind Centering. Contact Editions.

Boyd, J. E., Lanius, R. A., & McKinnon, M. C. (2018). Mindfulness-Based Treatments for Posttraumatic Stress Disorder: A Review of the Treatment Literature and Neurobiological Evidence. Journal of Psychiatry and Neuroscience, 43(1), 7–25. https://doi.org/10.1503/jpn.170021

Brook, A. (2001). From Conception to Crawling: Foundations for Developmental Movement. Body-Mind.Net.

Caldwell, C. (1996). Getting Our Bodies Back: Recovery, Healing, and Transformation through Body-Centered Psychotherapy. Shambhala.

Campbell, M., Decker, K. P., Kruk, K., & Deaver, S. P. (2016). Art Therapy and Cognitive Processing Therapy for Combat-Related PTSD: A Randomized Controlled Trial. Art Therapy, 33(4), 169–177. https://doi.org/10.1080/07421656.2016.1226643

Cascio, C. N., O'Donnell, M. B., Tinney, F. J., Lieberman, M. D., Taylor, S. E., Stretcher, V. J., & Falk, E. B. (2016). Self-Affirmation Activates Brain Systems Associated with Self-Related Processing and Reward and Is Reinforced by Future Orientation. Social Cognitive and Affective Neuroscience, 11(4), 621–629. https://doi.org/10.1093/scan/nsv136

Chevalier, G. (2015). The Effect of Grounding the Human Body on Mood. Psychological Reports, 116(2), 534–542. https://doi.org/10.2466/06.pr0.116k21w5

Chronic stress, cortisol dysfunction, and pain: A Psychoneuroendocrine rationale for stress management in pain rehabilitation. (n.d.). PubMed Central (PMC). https://www.ncbi.nlm.nih.gov/pmc/articles/PMC4263906/

Cohen, B. B., Nelson, L., & Smith, N. S. (2003). Sensing, Feeling, and Action: The Experiential Anatomy of Body-Mind Centering. Contact Editions.

Cornell, A. W. (1998). The Power of Focusing: A Practical Guide to Emotional Self-Healing. New Harbinger.

Hanna, T. (2004). Somatics: Reawakening the Mind's Control of Movement, Flexibility, and Health. Da Capo Press.

Heitzler, M. (2013). Broken Boundaries, Invaded Territories: The Challenges of Containment in Trauma Work. International Body Psychotherapy Journal, 28–41.

Hoshaw, C. (2021, February 26). Body Awareness: How to Deepen Your Connection with Your Body. Healthline. https://www.healthline.com/health/mind-body/body-awareness

(2022, December 27). How Box Breathing Can Help You Destress. Cleveland Clinic. https://health.clevelandclinic.org/box-breathing-benefits/

Levine, P. A. (2015). Trauma and Memory: Brain and Body in a Search for the Living Past: A Practical Guide for Understanding and Working with Traumatic Memory. North Atlantic Books.

Levine, P. A. (1997). Waking the Tiger—Healing Trauma: The Innate Capacity to Transform Overwhelming Experiences. North Atlantic Books.

Lowen, A. (1994). Bioenergetics: The Revolutionary Therapy That Uses the Language of the Body to Heal the Problems of the Mind. Arkana.

Moyers, T. B., & Rollnick, S. (2002). A Motivational Interviewing Perspective on Resistance in Psychotherapy. Journal of Clinical Psychology, 58(2), 185–193. https://doi.org/10.1002/jclp.1142

Ogden, P., & Fisher, J. (2015). Sensorimotor Psychotherapy: Interventions for Trauma and Attachment. W. W. Norton.

Ogden, P.,Minton, K., & Pain, C. (2006). Trauma and the Body: A Sensorimotor Approach to Psychotherapy. W. W. Norton.

Oschman, J. L., Chevalier, G., & Brown, R. (2015). The Effects of Grounding (Earthing) on Inflammation, the Immune Response, Wound Healing, and Prevention and Treatment of Chronic Inflammatory and Autoimmune Disease. Journal of Inflammation Research, 8, 83–96. https://doi.org/10.2147/JIR.S69656

Payne, H., Koch, S., Tantia, J., & Fuchs, T. (Eds.). (2019). The Routledge International Handbook of Embodied Perspectives in Psychotherapy: Approaches from Dance Movement and Body Psychotherapies. Routledge.

Payne, P., Levine, P., & Crane-Godreau, M. A. (2015). Somatic Experiencing: Using Interoception and Proprioception as Core Elements of Trauma Therapy. Frontiers in Psychology, 6, 93. https://doi.org/10.3389/fpsyg.2015.00093

Permanente, K. (n.d.). Forest bathing: What it is and why you should try it. https://healthy.kaiserpermanente.org/health-wellness/healtharticle.what-is-forest-bathing

Podvoll, E. M. (2003). Recovering Sanity: A Compassionate Approach to Understanding and Treating Psychosis. Shambhala.

R. (2020, January 14). Somatic Experiencing: A Body-Centered Approach to Treating PTSD. Lyn-Lake Psychotherapy & Wellness. https://therapy-mn.com/blog/somatic-experiencing-ptsd/

Schenck, L. (2017, March 6). Increase Somatic Awareness with a Body Scan Mindfulness Exercise. Mindfulness Muse. https://www.mindfulnessmuse.com/mindfulness-exercises/increase-somatic-awareness-with-a-body-scan-mindfulness-exercise

Schore, A. N., & Grotstein, J. S. (2016). Affect Regulation and the Origin of the Self: The Neurobiology of Emotional Development. Routledge.

Somatic experiencing for posttraumatic stress disorder: A randomized controlled outcome study. (n.d.). PubMed Central (PMC). https://www.ncbi.nlm.nih.gov/pmc/articles/PMC5518443/

Stress Management Versus Lifestyle Modification on Systolic Hypertension and Medication Elimination: A Randomized Trial. (n.d.) Mary Ann Liebert, Inc. https://www.liebertpub.com/doi/10.1089/acm.2007.0623

THC Editorial Team. (2022, January 26). Breathwork: Science, Types, and Benefits of Breathing Exercises. The Human Condition. https://thehumancondition.com/breathwork-science-types-benefits/

Traumatic stress: Effects on the brain. (n.d.). PubMed Central (PMC). https://www.ncbi.nlm.nih.gov/pmc/articles/PMC3181836/

Printed in Great Britain
by Amazon

47080395R00123